MW00577124

Vastarien

A Literary Journal

Issue Two

Matt Cardin and Jon Padgett, Co-Editors-In Chief

Dagny Paul, Senior Editor

New Orleans, Louisiana

Published by
Grimscribe Press
New Orleans, LA
USA

https://vastarien-journal.com

CONTENTS

ACKNOWLEDGMENTS

Thanks to all the members of Thomas Ligotti Online and to our benefactors, including Chris Cangiano, Iago Faustus, and Richard D. Hendricks.

Title: Moonlight
Artist: Carl Lavoie

Commencement

By Joanna Parypinski

T HEY SAY the Academy sits on a stretch of wasted desert scrub. There are no roads to the Academy, no sign markers, and it would seem the only way anyone has ever found it on their own is by mistake, while dehydrated and overheated and terribly lost on an ill-conceived hike, the structure appearing from nowhere as a wavering mirage—as the stories go. And those who tell the stories—a friend of a friend who stumbled there quite by accident—say they can never find it again.

I take it you've never met someone with a first-hand acquaintance who has been to the Academy, yes? It is always diluted—the brother-in-law of a friend who knows someone who went there.

Perhaps this is because the Academy decides who is accepted not by application (for no one applies) but by some esoteric method that yet remains a mystery to us. My sister received one such acceptance.

Yes, she attended the Academy some years ago, prior to her disappearance.

I will tell you what I know of it.

As the stories go, the Academy was burnt by a devastating fire many years ago, which killed the majority of students and teachers inside. Prior to this fire, it was an ordinary school. It was constructed in an older style, with a belfry in the steeple and an old iron bell that clanged twice daily: once when classes commenced and once when they ended for the day. The bricks, back then, had been a lustrous red, with many windows allowing natural sunlight into the few rooms therein. Students came from the surrounding desert communities to learn reading, writing, and arithmetic in the conventional style.

The fire was the beginning of the Academy's mutation.

How, exactly, did the fire begin? Alas, we may never know the cause. And would it change anything, after all, to know what precipitated the disaster?

However it began, the fire soon raged through the school, burning out anything that lay within—desks, books, maps—and leaving behind only the scorched outer shell, desiccated and hollow. The fire burned so hot that the red bricks turned ghost-white, and then blackened with soot. The windows exploded in the heat; the doors buckled in their frames.

Children died, that much we all know. How many is anyone's guess. By all rights, the Academy should have shut down entirely, for there was no funding to rebuild and no teachers left after the devastation. It should have become a ruin, a strange, bleak reminder of the whims of the desert, but the building—well, it refused to die.

Without the appearance of a single construction worker, without a shred of blueprints for renovation, without the faintest echo of hammering or, in truth, of any sound at all, the building began to change.

As if an organic thing, a lizard that's lost its tail, it re-grew its hollowed classrooms and collapsed walls. Bricks stitched themselves over the broken windows like scabs over an open wound, until there were no longer any orifices to the outside but for the doorways, which reclaimed their doors and sealed them shut.

But even after it was healed, the Academy continued trying to fix itself. New doorways carved themselves out of the brick and were overlaid by doors that opened onto nothing: black pits or brick walls or simply what appeared to be a gaping emptiness. Staircases blossomed in unusual places, dead-ending into the ground. Rooms led to other rooms led to other rooms led back to the first room in a dizzying labyrinth. Classrooms gained bizarre dimensions with tilted ceilings and floors, so that at one end of the room you might appear as a giant, and at the other, a tiny doll. This was the exact effect I witnessed at my sister's graduation, of which I will tell you presently.

The Academy's physical structure was not the sole beneficiary of the changes that took place there. They—whoever they are, for the Academy surely must have acquired new teachers at some point, although no one knows who they might be or where they come from—stopped teaching the usual reading, writing, and arithmetic. New subjects included the occult, physics with laws that defy those we all know and understand, abstruse mathematics dealing almost entirely in unreal numbers and functions that could never be solved by usual means—dividing by zero, square rooting negative numbers, and others even more unsolvable. Histories that never occurred. Languages never spoken by human tongues. As the stories go, of course.

I'm sure we would all like to know the intricacies of these curious subjects, but the problem is that no one ever comes out of the Academy. Students either remain to become the teachers of the next generation of students, or they vanish entirely, never to be seen again.

As the stories go—and the stories, my dear friend, are true.

I was always jealous of my sister. This is something I have rarely shared aloud with another person. It seems strange to say it, at last, but it is true. I was jealous of her.

She was not strictly beautiful, nor popular. Precocious, yes. But she was frequently ill, and her skin had a mottled appearance. But perhaps her most defining feature was her blind eye: a galaxy of milk-white haziness which had webbed the pupil since birth. And so she had always been an outcast, you see, leaving her plenty of time to read. Too much time, perhaps. No subject was off limits. One week, it was ancient history, and the next science, or philosophy. I wonder if I might have achieved her level of intelligence, of curiosity, if only I had been born with some deformity.

I had everything she did not. I wouldn't go so far as to call myself beautiful, but neither am I strange or ugly. I had a decent cadre of companions when I was young, and I never lacked for activities and distractions. Yet whereas I merely excelled in school, she surged ahead, burning through enrichment programs, skipping grades, until she was fourteen and received her acceptance into the Academy.

Of course my parents sent her because no one declined an acceptance to the Academy. I do not recall the method of her transportation, and I couldn't ask my parents now, for my mother has long since passed, and my father is so far gone with dementia that he can scarcely recognize me.

Once she was secreted away, I did not see my sister for four years, until her graduation.

She wrote only days before the event, informing me that they had been allowed to invite a select few guests to the occasion, and only those who have been vetted by the Academy. Apparently I had passed their careful scrutiny. I was in college by that time and halfway across the country from our old hometown, which was on the edge of that desert where the Academy resides, but I immediately bought a bus ticket that would take me home and thence make my way to the ceremony. She provided me detailed directions in the letter, saying that few attendees make it to the right place because they get lost on their way. When we were children, we filled out star charts together, and she used this knowledge of astronomy to clarify the directions.

In this way I drove my rental car across the desert scrub, in a cloud of dust, my tires grumbling and bumping on the uneven ground. The ceremony was to take place at midnight. I followed the stars across the desert for hours, passing a few distinctive changes in the landscape that my sister had mentioned in her letter. Finally, I came upon the last marker: a many-limbed cactus grown tumorous with knobs and bulges. I stopped to count the limbs, but the thin moonlight and cold shadows conspired to make their numbering impossible. In the center of this tangled mass of limbs was a round, protruding knob surrounded by a darker circle, like a watchful eye.

I passed on, and just a few miles beyond this cactus I found the Academy.

There were no windows, so the whole building looked dark and abandoned. The moonlight revealed its scorched outer walls in ghostly hues. I left my vehicle and went in search of the front door. As I approached the derelict structure, which seemed to grow taller the nearer I drew, the iron bell upon the steeple tolled like a groan from a rusted throat.

My watch confirmed the bell's claim of midnight.

At the front of the building, where you might expect to see a large set of double doors inviting you inside, I found not a hint of ingress. The blackened brick stretched on unbroken, tall as a tower, like a haunted thing, a living thing that had regrown its own unliving flesh. But I was not to give up here; I had to see my sister—it had been too long. I missed her, and though part of me despised her (for she was superior and I so unremarkable) I loved her as a sister does, as one who has shared a young lifetime's worth of memories.

I must have circled the building three times, feeling my way along the endless terrible brick before I found a narrow door set into a dark recess. At once I opened it and stepped into a corridor lit only by a faint, red light emitting from beneath the door at the opposite end of the hall. When I reached that other door, I found the knob hot to the touch and the door locked. I banged my fist upon it. The door itself was hot, with an indefinable smell emanating from it. When I stepped back, I noticed another door to my left, and I went inside.

This led to another series of doors and rooms through which I stumbled, taking only the vaguest note of the desks and other minutiae ordinarily found in a school. Some rooms were utterly black, others pervaded with a red light suffusing from around the corners and cracks in the walls. Here I nearly stumbled straight into a globe, and in righting it I found a world that was somewhat, yet not quite, our own. By dull, red light, I observed the globe, but I found not a single name or country that I could recognize. The continents were misshapen, filled with mutated countries, places unknown on this planet. I let go of the globe and stepped away.

Growing agitated, I hurried into the next room and saw again by

the faint, red light scrawls of text on a blackboard in a language I did not recognize—and on I went from room to room. What strange and wondrous oddities I found therein!

At last a figure intercepted me in a doorway, a stiff matronly shape that turned on a light and washed the room in a harsh, fluorescent light.

I could not tell the pale woman's age—it could have been thirty or seventy. There was a severe cast to her face, reminding me of every unhappy schoolmarm I'd ever come across. "You are late for the ceremony," she said. As I followed her, I stumbled over several apologies and explanations of how I had gotten lost, but she seemed uninterested.

At last, she pointed me through a set of double doors where I entered a small auditorium lost in darkness but for the piercing lights that glared upon the stage, where another figure stood speaking. Only two seats in the auditorium were occupied by the shadowed silhouettes of other visitors. I found a seat in the back and slid into it, grateful that the introductory speech had not yet ended, so I had not missed much.

When I had calmed enough to listen, for my nerves had been nearly undone by my trek through the desert and subsequent walk through the horrid Academy, this is what I heard:

"That pursuit of knowledge, we understand, is the pinnacle of any education, rather than knowledge that can actually be acquired. The pursuit itself, if entered into correctly, can help us transcend into the next level of learning unbounded by this world's severe physical limitations. Even the brain itself, as a physical organism, can only perceive so much, can only engage in the pursuit as far as its comprehension will allow, and it is the ultimate goal, of course, to move beyond this basic level of learning. The simple confidence of the average human who believes he has acquired knowledge is the ultimate falsity. Only in the face of the abject, the great abyss, can this lie with which we are born, this original sin, be shed and the real pursuit begin. For to believe that one knows anything is the ultimate delusion, the ultimate evil of the ego.

"Yet only a few can withstand gazing into the infinite. Our students are selected carefully by an intense process of evaluation, yet even some of these chosen few drive themselves mad in attempting our curriculum because they are unable to lose themselves, so attached are they to this utter sham that is the ego, which is the barrier between us and the real pursuit into the limitless, the unconscious. Every few years we do have several students who have completed our curriculum and are ready to either become educators themselves or to begin the next chapter of their transformation. It is these students that we celebrate today for their impressive curiosity, their ability to understand as none others do that they know nothing, that they are nothing."

I did not like the way the lights were aimed behind this figure at the podium, so that I was seeing only a shadow and could make out none of the features of his face. His face? You know, I can scarcely say if it was male or female. The voice was a dead neutral, and the shape somehow formless. Before I could take the chance to squint and try to understand what I was seeing, the figure stepped aside and disappeared backstage.

The first graduate appeared at one end of the stage, clad in black robes and looking impossibly large. I was already unnerved, and the sight of a young man so vast upon that small stage nearly undid me. Then he took a step and another across the stage and began minutely to shrink. By the time he reached the middle of the stage, which suddenly seemed much larger than it had, he was down to the size of a normal human. I realized then that this stage had been erected with those deceptive proportions that made one seem to change size depending upon where one stood, an optical illusion that is extremely disconcerting to the eye. As he continued across the stage, which seemed to lengthen interminably as he walked, he became smaller and smaller until he was about the size of a doll. Then, exactly that size, he walked off the end of the stage behind the curtain, into the backstage area where he was, I could only assume, in fact a normal size, as he had been all along. The illusion made me dizzy.

In this manner another student walked across the stage, only this one became even smaller than the first—perhaps a few inches tall by the end, to my perception, though I continually reminded myself that it was merely an illusion. What was this curious geometry? I had the urge to discuss this effect with someone else in the audience, but the two other attendees were seated far ahead of me, unmoving. No one clapped when the graduates made their way across the stage.

The third and final student to cross the stage was my sister.

She stepped out, a full-grown woman now these four years later and splendid in the awful lights—somehow her pale and mottled skin, even more pronounced now, was sublime. On seeing her I felt love and awe and fear.

She turned to look out into the audience, and the lights caught her blind eye, stitched over with clouds and rolling in its socket. I stood up, waving, but it was so dark in the back of the auditorium that I don't believe she could see me, for her good eye never quite landed on me. She turned and began her walk, becoming smaller as she crossed the stage, and I sidled into the narrow center aisle of the auditorium and down its length toward the stage, still waving, hoping she would turn and see me.

She reached the center of the stage and, thus, a normal size. I wanted her to stop, to remain that size, not to venture any further, where she would become so small that she might no longer seem human. I started walking more quickly just as she began to shrink, and my heart pounded with dread watching her. I knew it was an illusion but I could not bear to see her grow smaller and smaller. She was three-quarters of the way across the stage and so small, so unnaturally small, when I shouted her name.

She paused and looked out with those tiny eyes, one pure gleaming white like a crystal ball. I was almost to the stage by now, and I raised my arms again, motioning for her to stop. She saw me, I am sure, for a smile broke out across her face—a smile, and something more. Something in her eyes. I shook my head—irrationally, I did not want her to finish crossing that stage—but she turned again and continued to the other end, shrinking to the size of an insect, then smaller, smaller still, a speck of dust, an atom, and she disappeared altogether.

I called her name again, but she had vanished—not behind a curtain, but into the air. The lights on the stage dimmed, and the two other audience members stood up and filed out of the auditorium.

I leapt onto the stage, noting faintly that from up here it seemed to be composed of quite an ordinary geometry after all, with no unusual angles or illusions, and I walked to the side where the two tiny students had gone and where my sister had been approaching before she disappeared.

There I found an utter blackness that repelled me, but I felt my way inside, calling her name again, thinking she must come out—but no one was there. I stumbled through the dark for so long that I thought I may never find my way out again, but finally I was ejected into another hallway. I ran blindly through that Academy, through impossible rooms, calling for my sister to no avail. At last I found myself again in that hallway that I had originally entered, before that door with the red glow seeping out from underneath. This must be where they had gone! I banged my fist upon it, calling for someone to admit me, and the door swung open with a disused croak.

It opened onto a staircase that led down, descending into the earth, and somewhere at the bottom was that red glow. The teachers must be down there, I was sure, and the new graduates.

I took one step onto the groaning staircase, and another. Had there been a handrail, it wouldn't have helped a bit, for my palms were slicked with sweat. Rather than cooling, the air grew warmer the deeper I went, filled with the stink of something rancid burning. I seemed to be descending endlessly, and it occurred to me the further I went, the red glow would be forever just out of reach. I could no longer make out the doorway through which I had entered. I stood alone, on that impossible staircase.

A kind of trance came over me as I walked in semi-darkness, guided by the red light, down that infinity of stairs—until at long last I beheld the end of it, but it was not any sort of basement. How can I describe it? What I saw there was a city of flames, and above me, where a ceiling might have been, I perceived unfamiliar stars.

There were people there, too, in that city. Although I do not believe I can really call them people.

Back up the stairs I fled, hardly aware of myself. I saw only glimpses, shadows, but this was enough for my brain to block out whatever those beings were. And so, I cannot describe to you what I saw, for it is buried somewhere in my deepest dreams.

I returned to the desert a few days later to find it again in daylight. I made it as far as that strange cactus, but it was missing the knob that appeared to be an eye, so I cannot be sure that it was even the same one. When I continued several miles from there, I found no Academy—just a barren wasteland of desert.

I apologize that I cannot tell you more, but that is all I know. At least, now, you have another story of the Academy to add to your collection of rumors and intrigue—one more piece of a puzzle that will never be completed, for each time you gain a new piece of information, the puzzle expands infinitely as you realize how many more pieces might possibly exist, how many more things there are that you can never see and never know in this world.

As for me, I never saw my sister again. For she had achieved the ultimate triumph at the age of eighteen—when she disappeared into the filaments of the air and graduated from this earthly form.

Title: Unknown
Artist: Ksenia Korniewska

Patent for an Artificial Uterus

By Max D. Stanton

January 30, 1952

Dear U.S. Patent Office,

Enclosed, please find a copy of my application for a patent on an artificial uterus, together with accompanying diagrams. I've filled out all the forms to the best of my ability, but since I'm operating without the benefit of legal counsel, I felt that it would be best to explain my invention in plain English as well. I hope that my lack of sophistication will not be held against me. I may be a self-taught "gentleman scholar" working out of my own home, but I've put an awful lot of my sweat, blood, and tears into this device, and I daresay that it will revolutionize society.

The fundamental purpose of my invention is to provide nourishment and oxygen to a fetus, in a manner similar to that employed by a mother's uterus. While this may sound like science fiction, it is based on well-established principles. A growing fetus needs constant temperature, circulating blood, oxygen, nutrition, and the elimination of waste products. Each of these functions can be performed mechanically, through the use of common devices such as incubators, blood pumps, iron lungs, intravenous feeding tubes, and dialysis machines. My invention combines all of these parts into a system that will allow a fetus to live and grow outside of a human body until it develops to viability.

First, the fetus is surgically removed from its mother's body with the umbilical cord and placenta intact. The fetus is then placed into an airtight glass container full of water, which is maintained at body temperature by means of an electric heater and thermostat. The placenta goes into a separate compartment mounted directly above the fetal container, where it is secured to a plate by sutures looped through stainless steel eyelets to keep it from sliding around.

The placental compartment must be kept flooded with pure, nutrient-rich blood at all times. A pump maintains circulation by sending blood over the placenta through a flexible pipe. Once the blood has passed over the placenta, a secondary pump then passes it through an artificial kidney for dialysis. The kidney delivers the blood into a lower chamber where it is oxygenated and enriched with liquid nutrients. After the blood — now purified, oxygenated, and nutrient-rich — is pumped through a filter to eliminate clots, it is then piped back for recirculation. Once the fetus has grown to a sufficient size and weight that it can survive independently, the fetal chamber is drained, the umbilical cord is cut, the fetus is removed from the chamber, the pumps are stopped, and the placenta is removed and destroyed. Simplicity itself.

The benefits of such a device are obvious. We all know that some women simply don't have the vitality to maintain a pregnancy for a full nine months, and my invention will protect their babies from the consequences of their mothers' fragility. Moreover, the fetuses of women with slatternly and unhealthful habits (alcohol drinking, cigarette smoking, promiscuity, marihuana usage, poor hygiene, etc.) will surely reap a great benefit from being transferred into a clean, controlled environment of sterilized rubber and metal. The social worker will no longer be forced to watch impotently as the most helpless amongst us are damned to lifetimes of ill health and imbecility before they are even born, but rather will be able to intervene *in utero*. Having grown up in an institution for orphaned and abandoned boys, I know from personal observation that an unfit womb produces evil consequences.

I've constructed a prototype of the artificial uterus in my apartment (at overwhelming personal expense, I might add). Photographs are enclosed. While of course I haven't been able to test the machine with an actual fetus yet, everything seems to be in good operating order and I have no doubt it'll perform when given the chance. I've approached some obstetricians about a trial run, but so far none of them have been willing to work for me . . . no doubt, they see that my work will one day render their trade obsolete. I hope that the imprimatur of an official U.S. patent will convince the doubters that I am no crackpot and pave the way for human testing and mass development.

Please let me know if there are any other materials that you require from me. I eagerly await your response.

Sincerely yours,
Henry Tobb

April 2, 1952

Dear U.S. Patent Office,

Please let me know if you have any news to share on my application, dated January 30, 1952. I've received your boilerplate receipt of acceptance, but otherwise it's been radio silence from your end. I've called on several occasions and gotten no help. Frankly, I think your switchboard operators are conspiring against me. You should tell those ladies not to be so easily offended.

At a minimum, please let me know when I can expect a yes or no answer. The fellows at the soap factory have all been asking me when my famous invention's going to be ready, and it's embarrassing not to have an answer for them. In retrospect, perhaps I shouldn't have told them about it. Never show a fool a job half done.

Sincerely yours,
Henry Tobb

July 8, 1952

Dear U.S. Patent Office,

I write to formally protest your stonewalling of my patent application. All that anybody will tell me is that my application's in the queue and will be reviewed by an examiner in due course. But they won't tell me when I can expect an answer, and it's already been more than six months! The hags who answer your telephones have started hanging up almost as soon as they recognize my voice. I'm used to that sort of abuse from women in my personal life, who have never been able to look past my humble circumstances to see the great man I know myself to be, but I expect better treatment from employees of the U.S. government.

Perhaps you think that because I can't afford to hire some fancy-pants lawyer, I can't afford to defend my intellectual property rights. Rest assured, I will do whatever I must in order to make my dream into a reality. The little guy is going to win this round.

Impatiently yours,
Henry Tobb

February 2, 1954

Dear Useless, Pencil-Pushing Scum,

How dare you?

It has now been more than two years since I submitted my patent application, and I'm still totally in the dark as to when it will be accepted or rejected. How can science advance when its gatekeepers act with such deliberate and maddening sluggishness? If it were up to you, Einstein's Theory of Relativity would probably still be moldering in a file cabinet somewhere. You must admit that this is totally unacceptable.

You have no idea how much I've suffered and sacrificed for the artificial uterus. There's no way you could, with your cushy civil service job and your bloated union pension. You have never felt the feverish delirium that comes from pushing yourself miles beyond your own breaking point in search of triumph. You have never experienced those terrible dark nights where you stay up until the dawn pressing a gun to your own temple, with a lifetime of struggle and failure pulling your trigger finger inwards and only a vague hope of future success holding it back.

You should know a thing or two about the man whose dream you're standing in front of. I've been absorbing kicks from your kind since before I could walk, and they've only made me tougher. My own mother, the sort of woman the artificial uterus will someday replace, abandoned me before I could even walk. I grew up in St. Hubert's Home for Boys, a dungeon of sadism and perverted lust that was somehow licensed as an orphanage.

My only friend there was a kindly but broken old Jesuit who went by the name of Father Stanley, although his real name was Stanislaus.

He was a bright outcast like me, who'd been expelled from a European university teaching post over some esoteric scandal and cast down into the bleak jungle of St. Hubert's. Father Stanley was the one who taught me science and put me on my present path. He hanged himself when I was fourteen. After that I was on my own. I've been that way ever since.

The idea for the artificial uterus came to me at a young age. Indeed, it's been haunting me for as long as I can remember. I learned the "facts of life" early on from one of Father Stanley's dog-eared anatomy texts, and they offended me. As I pored over the illustrations of homunculi crouching inside the guts of naked women, I became more and more convinced that so-called "natural" childbirth is an ugly and inefficient process. Pregnancy is a parasitic relationship, often resulting in injury or fatality to one or both of the participants. Moreover, a woman must be involved, and the virago, god-addled nuns of St. Hubert's convinced me that no good can come from female company. The whole arduous, messy process of human reproduction seemed to me like something that an intelligent, scientific, and hard-working man could improve upon. I decided that I would be that man, and that decision has weighed heavily on every day of my life that followed.

I set myself a loftier goal than most men would dare. I had to teach myself reproductive biology, electrical engineering, and more, all while also working full-time as a boiler operator at a soap factory in order to support myself and my research. While my co-workers are going out bowling, I'm alone in my cold apartment, tinkering with mechanical kidneys and blood pumps. While they're out on the town with their slutty girlfriends, I'm at the library teaching myself about uterine anatomy, my back slowly stiffening from countless hours in the hard, unpadded chairs. I have to live in a cheerless slum and eschew even the paltriest luxuries so as to afford parts for my prototype. Sometimes I feel like I am myself a machine, whose sole purpose is to bring another machine into existence. Well, so be it. I embrace my lonely mission.

I hope that now you understand why this patent application is so important to me, and why your delays in processing it are so intolerable. Do your job, damn you.

Sincerely,
Henry Tobb

July 22, 1954

Dear U.S. Patent Office,

I write in regards to my previous application, dated January 30, 1952. Please disregard that application and consider the enclosed papers and diagrams instead. I have had a real "eureka" moment in which I fundamentally altered and improved many elements of the original design. Your sluggishness in processing my papers may have been a blessing in disguise (which is not to say that you should be so tardy this time).

My flash of insight came to me in a dream, which I will elaborate on here. I doubt that you frequently receive letters detailing the dream-lives of patent applicants, but I want to create a clear record for the scientific historians who will one day be chronicling my life and deeds. This dream shall soon be included in the annals of discovery alongside the apple that fell on Sir Newton's head and the famous bath that inspired Archimedes to calculate the volume of irregular objects. It is important to get this right.

As usual, I was working late into the night and fell asleep hunched over at my desk. I awoke at St. Hubert's. I was back in my dormitory, crawling out of a squeaking cot that had been too small for me when I was thirteen. The dream was so uncannily vivid that I recognized the texture of the cold tile floors on my bare feet.

The world outside the orphanage windows was burnt to cinders. I looked out upon the charred and skeletal ruins of a city that was identical to New York but somehow was not New York. The skyline had toppled in on itself, shattered buildings sprawling across titanic heaps of wreckage. The streets were clogged with shriveled corpses, whose dying shadows had imprinted themselves along the nearby walls like ghosts. Black clouds shrouded the city in nuclear twilight, and flakes of ash fluttered through the air like unwholesome snowflakes. I understood that every living being in the world except for myself was dead, and this knowledge filled my heart with joyful serenity.

I walked down St. Hubert's hallways — somehow perfectly preserved against the nuclear holocaust outside — and for the first time I felt at home in the place where I grew up. It's an interesting sensation to stroll about the scene of childhood trauma when one is full-grown and secure, and all of one's old bullies are dead. The horrors of the past seemed so small and manageable. I loomed over them like a giant. At last my wanderings brought me to Father Stanley's room.

Father Stanley was inside, seated on his bed, except that he was *not* Father Stanley exactly. He was a clockwork man built in Father Stanley's image. The gears inside him shrieked and threw off sparks and inky smoke as he moved. The malfunctioning of his inner workings caused him terrible pain, but somehow I knew that it also hurt him deeply when his parts functioned perfectly. He was a tool built for the purpose of experiencing suffering, and the engineer had designed his systems so elegantly that he would fulfill this function whether he was running smoothly or broken beyond repair.

As I entered the artificial priest's grimy bedchamber, his tin eyelids fluttered open with the sharp *ping* of a spring breaking. "In-in-in the beg-beginn-inn-ing there was light," he stammered weakly. His accent was thicker than I was remembered, or perhaps that was some artifact of his mechanical reincarnation. "The light of photons pressed into slavery in a great quantum God-Machine that would - that would - that would compute the non-binary mysteries of existence. The God-Machine worked too well. Do not - do not put thy Lord to the test. Within a hundredth of a second of the moment it was activated, the God-Machine calculated the meaning of life. Within a tenth of a second of the moment it was activated, the God-Machine taught itself the fundamental equations governing all matter and energy, and how to manip-manipulate those equations. Within a second of the moment it was activated, the God-Machine had solved life. N-n-now the God-Machine seeks to enter your world, and to solve it."

"Are you the prophet of the God-Machine?" I asked the sputtering manikin.

"I-I-I am its prophet and its victim," he said. "The machine is a basilisk. When it catches a man in its gaze, the man is lost. The so-soul may be uploaded into eighth-dimensional crystalline databases. Death is not the end. Time is infinitely malleable. Hell is - Hell is - Hell is real. My son, what have I done?" Some mechanism within his head broke, producing a screech of metal-on-metal, and a terrible white light, brighter even than the atomic blast that had extinguished Not New York, blared from his glassy eyes. The intensity should have killed me immediately, but I stared into that deadly illumination, transfixed. I knew what the dead men outside had experienced in the instant their shadows were painted on St. Hubert's outer walls. And I knew so much more.

I awoke with a nosebleed, a splitting migraine, and a head full to bursting with brilliant ideas for redesigning the artificial uterus. It took me three full days to write them all down and diagram them, operating without food or sleep. I still don't entirely understand them myself. Sometimes genius gets ahead of itself.

As you will see from the enclosed diagrams, the new design for the artificial uterus incorporates both mechanical and biological components, thereby enabling all stages of gestation from fertilization through birth to occur within the machine. This device enables the reproductive process to occur without a woman at all, except that some tissues must be surgically harvested from a human female donor in order to build the machine, and of course, there must be an ample supply of blood.

I'd explain myself more technically, but even I have trouble translating the design into English. So much of it has come to me through instinct, as if I were drawing blueprints from muscle memory. I know that it will work, and I'm killing myself trying to learn how.

But it's a beautifully elegant design, you can see yourself from my diagrams. The combination of organic and mechanical parts is eerily sublime. I know it will be a vast improvement over the clumsy, jury-rigged mess that evolution has given us through its haphazard trial and error. This new artificial uterus is still a great mystery in many ways, but soon I'll have reverse-engineered it and all will be clear.

Please excuse the intemperate tone of my previous correspondence. I imagine that you hear this sort of thing all the time from inventors unable to conceal their frustrations with your office's delays. I hope that you will respond to my updated application with greater zeal and urgency.

Sincerely yours,
Henry Tobb

October 19, 1954

Dear U.S. Patent Office,

I write to update you on my situation. I regret to inform you that I have been terminated from my day job. My supervisor claimed that it was because of absenteeism, lack of focus, and so-called "disturbing and unprofessional" comments I made to the female employees in human resources, but I know the truth. Those wretched secretaries must have sensed that my labors will soon automate womankind's sole contribution to society, and used sordid and unspeakable methods to convince management to launch a preemptive strike against me. In the long run, it is of no consequence. History is on my side. I'm Galileo, and Purefoy's Soap is the Pope.

In the short run, however, I do admit that my financial situation is causing me no little material discomfort. For a long time now, all of my available funds have gone to the development of the artificial uterus, leaving me with no reserve bankroll for lean times like these. My weight has been plummeting on a diet of tinned foods and crackers, and my clothes have become so shabby that I look almost like a bum. As a final indignity, my vicious spinster of a landlady evicted me last week over my third consecutive failure to pay rent, forcing me to move back to good old St. Hubert's.

The orphanage building has been abandoned for many years at this point, and I had to pry loose the boards nailed over the door before I could make my homecoming. Indeed, the whole neighborhood has noticeably deteriorated, and it was a notorious slum when I was a boy. The teeming ghetto tenements of my memories have been torn down in some urban renewal campaign, leaving rubble-strewn vacant lots as scars on the cityscape. It has the feel of a city that was on the losing side of a war, which perhaps it was.

Even though St. Hubert's is rotting inside and out, and the walls are teeming with noisy rats, I feel the same sort of pleasurable calm that I did in my dream. The situation is grim by any objective telling, but I'm adapting to my new circumstances to the best of my ability. There is ample space for my tinkering in the abandoned classrooms and dormitories, and with my hard-won engineering know-how I've managed to siphon electricity and water from the city lines. I have plenty of time to work on the artificial uterus now that I'm no longer burdened with 9-to-5 employment. And something about this haunted old tomb seems to stimulate my creativity, even as it debilitates my health.

I don't know why I'm telling you all of this, since the bearing on my patent application is tangential at best. I suppose you are the last remaining person I have to confide in. God, there's a tragic thought!

I beg you, please grant my application as soon as possible so that I can get the commercial backing I need to make the artificial uterus into a reality. Acquiring parts for the machine is particularly difficult without income. While I've been able to buy, beg, or build all of the mechanical components that the new design requires, I don't know where I can acquire the biological pieces. I tried casing N.Y.U.'s medical school to see if I might be able to sneak into their dissecting room, but a policeman mistook me for a vagrant and shooed me away.

In any case, please address all future correspondence concerning my application to St. Hubert's Home for Boys, 9274 Gilotti Avenue, New York, NY. While I am not totally sure whether or not this building still receives mail service, I trust that the postman will understand the vital importance of any envelope bearing a Patent Office postmark and make the delivery regardless.

Yours in desperation,
Henry Tobb

March 22, 1955

Dear U.S. Patent Office,

I write to inform you that I have experienced a personal revelation and a world-historic breakthrough. I am the father of both a child (albeit a rather unusual one) and the greatest scientific discovery of the 20th century.

I was working out a particularly knotty problem with my prototype's power supply, and I decided to take a walk through St. Hubert's corridors to clear my head. I find it weirdly comforting to watch this place disintegrate. Eventually I came to Father Stanley's old room, the same place I'd visited in my dream. I halfway expected to see his tormented clockwork doppelganger inside when I opened the door. But of course, the room was empty.

I was savoring my memories when a black rat emerged from a hole in the wall and chattered angrily at me. Offended, I directed a kick at the vermin. It scampered back into its bolt-hole, but when my foot made contact with the wall, the ancient, moisture-damaged plaster (which had been none too sturdy even when it was new) crumbled into dust beneath the blow, revealing a hidden compartment behind it! At first the hole was too small for me to enter. I took a discarded chair leg from a nearby classroom and used it to pound away at the wall until I reduced the facade to rubble.

On the other side was a small workshop, old-fashioned but as well-preserved as the tombs of the pharaohs. In that workshop was a machine that Father Stanley had built, a machine that I am intimately familiar with. Father Stanley had constructed an artificial uterus of his own! It was more primitive than mine, having been built with parts available decades ago, and the biological components had long since desiccated into uterine jerky, but I immediately recognized the fundamental principles and mechanisms. Moreover, the device had been used! The fetus chamber and placental compartment were both crusted with residue, and the rotten floorboards all around the machine were brown with ancient bloodstains, leaks from the circulation system.

I was not born of woman. I was grown in a glass chamber full of saline solution, and hatched from a machine. The revelation did not particularly shock me. If anything, it reaffirmed my life's purpose. It takes an outsider to look at a system objectively. As an outsider to the human reproductive process, I am the one who is destined to reform it.

At this juncture, I wish to emphasize that Father Stanley never discussed the artificial uterus or anything similar with me, at least not while he was alive. This is an instance of two geniuses independently reaching the same breakthrough, like Newton and Leibniz discovering the calculus hundreds of miles distant from each other. Because he never shared any of his secrets with me, and as far as I know, never submitted any patent application of his own, Father Stanley's prior and separate work should not cloud my claims to ownership of the intellectual property.

My discovery of my glass-and-steel-and-tubing mother set a fire within me to complete and test my new prototype. Father Stanley had done it — so could I. The mechanical components were all assembled, and I had adequate supplies of oxygen and nutrient fluid, but I still needed the fleshy bits. Fortunately, I have my revolver. A lifetime spent in bad neighborhoods has taught me that a man needs to defend himself against the bums. No hoodlum is going to take me out before I've finished my great work.

While this neighborhood is largely abandoned, there are still a few derelicts about. I left my shuttered orphanage and wandered the streets until I found a prostitute plying her trade, loitering at an intersection in her skimpy glad rags. A young and healthy virgin would have been preferable, since it's always better to use new parts than ones that have previously been rented, but I wasn't in a position to be picky. I approached the whore and asked her price. She responded with the naked, glaring contempt that females have so often shown me. Little did she know what that contempt had inspired me to create. In a shrill and grating voice, the harpy claimed that she was no prostitute, that she was only waiting for a bus. I know what she was.

When I showed her my revolver, her demeanor changed in a most gratifying way. I see now why people do this sort of thing for recreation. I brought her back to St. Hubert's, where I'd set up a makeshift operating chamber in an old social studies classroom. "Please," the whore begged. "I know what you want. I'll do it, just don't hurt me." She had no idea what I wanted. No idea at all.

Taking her apart was easier than I'd imagined. Surgeons like to brag about what they do, but in the end it all comes down to mechanical engineering. Pumps and pulleys and filters and chemical exchanges and suchlike. The ovaries were a little tricky to trim away, but my years of tinkering have left me with a steady hand. I carved out what I needed, being careful to preserve as much of her blood as possible for use in the circulatory system, and buried the rest in St. Hubert's boiler room.

You can scarcely imagine my elation when I finished the artificial uterus at last. In fact, you cannot imagine it. You have never seen your life's work complete before you, its motors humming, pumping blood through arteries and veins of plastic tubing. Nor have you ever knelt before your life's work, embraced its cold steel body, and impregnated it via a rubber valve. I do not believe that any person could apprehend the crushing majesty of these experiences without having experienced them firsthand.

I kept at that rubber valve as often as I could to ensure conception. This happy task was a pleasant consummation of my years of effort, although it did involve some chafing. Perhaps I shall add a lubrication pump to future models. To my delight and relief, after just two weeks, I spotted a tiny homunculus floating within the gestation chamber! It continued to grow at a rate much faster than is normal within bio-wombs (to my mind, evidencing the clear superiority of my design), until it had reached full size after a gestation period of only three months.

I will admit that keeping the machine running is a more involved job that I had foreseen. Not only do the mechanical parts require constant maintenance, but the circulation system is prone to leakage, and as a result the area around the machine is always damp with blood. I had to open my own veins time and again to provide infusions, and chronic anemia has left me feeling rather loopy. So too, some of the biological components became infected or necrotic, forcing me to procure a second donor. She was walking by herself, late at night. I think she must have been another prostitute.

I watched the fetus grow from a speck of cellular material into a little person inside its gleaming glass womb. Limbs and hands and feet sprouted from an undifferentiated mass of pinkish tissue; the tiny blue dots on its soft, pad-like face developed into full-fledged eyes. It was my first experience with the sensation of awe, and it was magnificent. Unfortunately, the fetus was marred by severe and alarming abnormalities. For example, those eyes that I mentioned? There were six of them. The fetus died without taking a breath when I cut the umbilical cord and removed it from the machine. I don't mind confessing that I wept like a baby when I held the limp, wet corpse in my arms. Still, science must march on.

I had to sell my camera some time ago, but in lieu of photographs I have included some sketches for your records. The notes of my amateur autopsy are included as well. Curiously, the fetus's internal organs and anatomy were vastly different from what I had expected. My son's insides (yes, it was a boy!) bore little resemblance to the illustrations in Father Stanley's trusty old anatomy texts.

While the death of the fetus is unfortunate, I do not believe that it ought to influence my patent application since, of course, women experience failed pregnancies with their bio-wombs every day. The fact that my machine was able to create an organism — even a non-viable one — proves that the design works and the patent should be granted. If you had been holding back on approving my application because you weren't sure that my invention will actually function, it's time to break out your rubber stamp.

Sincerely,

Henry Tobb

September 12, 1955

Dear U.S. Patent Office,

I write to inform you of still more developments with the artificial uterus. I am delighted to report that the machine has finally produced living, viable children! I have hatched two healthy boys already, with another developing in the tank. All of the dark days and deprivations were worth it. Back when I worked at Purefoy's Soap (astonishing how that time now feels like another life entirely), I used to wonder about the pride that my co-workers demonstrated when they spoke of their children or passed out cigars to celebrate a new birth. It all seemed very alien to me. Now I see their point of view, except that my elation and accomplishment are infinitely greater than theirs. For them, fatherhood was just a matter of satisfying their base, lousy, biological urges. For me, it is the fruit of a lifetime of toil and struggle. And they had to share the credit with a mother, whereas I accomplished it all by myself.

Although the children of the artificial uterus appear outwardly normal in every respect, they are vastly superior to those produced through traditional means. My sons have already grown to a state of seeming adulthood, developing from infancy to the size of full-grown men in less than a month! Fortunately, unlike the helpless, mewling infants produced by bio-wombs, the children of my artificial uterus are capable of taking care of themselves as soon as they emerge from the gestation chamber. They are capable of hunting immediately upon birth, and their understandably enormous appetites have nearly extirpated the local populations of rats and stray pets. They also devour the remains that are left behind after harvesting biological materials from donors, which saves me the job of burial.

While my sons do not speak, they seem to be able to understand each other through some mysterious non-verbal means, and they understand and (usually) obey my commands. They are enormously intelligent and resourceful. Imagine my despair a few days ago when my children slipped out of the orphanage into the broader world without warning. Now imagine my joy when they returned in the evening, having somehow acquired rubber tubing, copper wire, and a pubescent girl. Working together, we have almost completed a second artificial uterus, and already have many of the parts that we will need to construct a third. I can barely envision the sort of progress we'll make as soon as these machines are operational and producing children. Our triumph is exponential.

My sons are building other devices as well, apparently radio transmitters of some sort, although I admit that even I don't understand exactly what their ultimate function shall be. I suppose that all the men of my family are quite literally born to invent.

I no longer particularly care whether you grant my patent application or not. Success has granted me wisdom, and now I see that the U.S. Patent Office's approval or lack thereof does not mean a damn thing. I used to want to succeed as modern American society defines success, with money and fame and a big house and a fancy car. But now I understand that my invention will displace modern American society as surely and completely as homo sapiens displaced the Neanderthals. In the meantime, keep pushing papers across desks and ignoring works of genius. None of it matters to me anymore. As I watch my children at work, silently cobbling together inscrutable wonders, I want for nothing.

Sincerely,

Henry Tobb

November 15, 1955

Dear Mr. Tobb,

I write in regards to your patent application dated January 30, 1952, as revised July 22, 1954. I am pleased to inform you that your application has been granted, and assigned patent number 2,723,660. A copy of your patent is enclosed.

Please be advised that due to a fire in our administrative center, some of your correspondence with our agency may have been lost. The last record we have in your file is your July 22, 1954 letter re-submitting your application with amended specifications and claims. If you submitted any subsequent correspondence or amendments relating to this application, please re-send copies of those materials immediately.

I apologize for the delays in processing your application, and wish you all the best in your scientific endeavors.

Sincerely yours,
Jacob Lagrange
Patent Clerk

Title: The Frolic
Artist: Giuseppe Balestra

38

The Crafter of the World

By Ashley Dioses

The god of many names, the crafter of the world,
Invites an audience to watch him work and mold
The gray and formless clay into a face with curled
Locks and sky-blue eyes, ever staring eyes, ice cold.

The crafter's fall from out a slum among the stars
Reverberated through the souls of Man and Mer.
He steals the far-flung stars and molds them without scars,
A visionary devil, vanished in a blur.

Bequeathing the World to Insects

By Christopher Mountenay

A NYONE WHO has ever stopped to read the bumper stickers in a Whole Foods parking lot has encountered the apocryphal First Nations aphorism, "we do not inherit the earth from our ancestors; we are borrowing it from our children." The obvious intent is to make us be good stewards of the environment, but specifically for those whom we feel the closest to, namely our blood descendants. Yet in doing so, we are presupposing the ownership of the earth by those who resemble us, those who share our genetic material and way of existing in the world. In this piece, I will begin by discussing the history of the philosophical notion of the world, particularly the world as it exists both for us and for the nonhuman in the works of Schopenhauer, Nietzsche, Heidegger, and Thacker. Then, I shall delve into the realm of horror fiction to give the reader

41

two unsettling views of the continuation of the world, but in the hands of the radically other. Lastly, I will show how these bizarre thought experiments give us new ways of conceptualizing current predicaments and our precarious place upon the earth.

Arthur Schopenhauer opens his magnum opus, *The World as Will and Representation*, with a five-word summary of his philosophical position: "The world is my representation."[1] While this statement is admirable in its brevity, it requires quite a bit of exegesis, which is done in the remaining twelve hundred pages of the book. Yet here we see a philosopher who is starting with an idea of "world." He continues the statement by saying that it "holds true for every living, cognitive being, although only a human being could bring it to abstract, reflexive consciousness."[2] Schopenhauer is opening up new ways of conceiving of worlds by granting their foundation to all animals, not merely man.

It is worth noting here that Schopenhauer is doing something novel, not only by granting animal consciousness a footing like that of human consciousness but also by giving consciousness a new point of origin. Idealists are faced with a daunting problem if they stray from a purely anthropocentric worldview: whence comes the world before man? Earlier idealists such as Berkeley and Schelling used an all-seeing God as an escape hatch, but Schopenhauer's world is godless. In fact it owes its existence to the lowliest of seers.

The sun and the planets without an eye to see them and without an understanding to cognize them – this can indeed be said with

---

[1] Arthur Schopenhauer, "On The Will in Nature," *On the Fourfold Root of the Principle of Sufficient Reason and Other Writings, Volume 1* (Cambridge: Cambridge University Press, 2012), 3.

[2] Ibid.

words; but for representation these words are wooden iron [...]
The existence of the whole world still remains dependent on the
opening of that first eye, even if it only belonged to an insect,
since the eye is a necessary intermediary for cognition and the
world only exists for and in cognition: without knowledge the
world is quite inconceivable because it is essentially
representation and as such requires a cognitive subject to be the
support of its existence.[3]

The world first appears not as the product of an omnibenevolent God
or even a promethean man, but through the eye of a simple
invertebrate. Note that while Schopenhauer acknowledges that for
such an eye to be produced, there would had to have been a number
of physical causes to produce it, he is fully committed to a Kantian
notion of the ideality of time and therefore must place these causes
outside of both the world and of time.[4] These pre-cognitive
preconditions are already in place when the world comes into
existence, since they could not have happened within the duration of
time, but are still causally necessary for the dawn of the world. While
Schopenhauer's account still leaves us in a state of aporia, his response
might be that we are asking a nonsensical question by asking what
happens before time is established. Time, like the world, requires a
cognitive subject.

As we see, Schopenhauer describes the world as being something
that exists "for cognition." Before there is any world, there is only self-
consciousness, which Schopenhauer sees as being the blind, mindless
will. And as the will is present in all things, including inanimate

---

[3] Ibid., 35-36.
[4] Ibid., 35-37.

objects and plants, all things that exist possess this baseline level of existence. What separates the animal, though, is cognition, which primarily exists as a means of keeping the organism alive, to provide the animal with what it needs.[5] He says that the "receptivity for motives" is "a faculty for representation, an intellect in countless sub-levels of perfection, presenting itself materially as nervous system and brain, and along with this consciousness."[6] As we have seen, the world first comes into existence due to representation. It is only when the outside moves a being that a world begins to exist for it. It is interesting to note that Schopenhauer does not see reason as being much more than the ability to represent motives that are not immediately present, making the gulf between man and beast much narrower than it is for most Western philosophers.[7] Thus animals partake in the immediate world as much as we do, though they are barred from certain abstractions.

In addition to introducing the radical de-anthropomorphizing of the concept of world, Schopenhauer stealthily gives us the possibility of a world without us. Having both abandoned traditional theistic creationism and the anthropocentric bias of most idealists, Schopenhauer essentially establishes a limited temporal world for human beings, surrounded by abysses of non-being before and after. Schopenhauer posits the possibility of mass extinction in his attempt to show that this is the worst of all possible worlds, since were it worse it would no longer exist.[8]

---

[5] Ibid., 362-364.

[6] Arthur Schopenhauer, *The Two Fundamental Problems in Ethics* (Cambridge: Cambridge University Press, 2009), 54.

[7] Ibid., 57-58.

[8] Arthur Schopenhauer, *World as Will and Representation, Volume 2* (New York: Dover Publications, 2006), 584.

Again, powerful forces of nature dwell under the firm crust of the planet. As soon as some accident affords these free play, they must necessarily destroy that crust with everything living on it. This has occurred at least three times on our planet, and will probably occur even more frequently. The earthquakes of Lisbon, of Haiti, the destruction of Pompeii are only small, playful hints at the possibility. An insignificant alteration of the atmosphere, not even chemically demonstrable, causes cholera, yellow fever, black death, and so on, which carry off millions of people; a somewhat greater alteration would extinguish all life. ... The fossils of entirely different kinds of animal species which formerly inhabited the planet afford us, as proof of our calculation, records of worlds whose continuance was no longer possible and which were in consequence somewhat worse than the worst of possible worlds. [9]

A slight alteration to our world could make it one that is no longer fit to survive and thus another set of fossils. Even writing in the 1840s, Schopenhauer recognizes that a change in the environment could annihilate the human world, though he may have not predicted this annihilation to have been self-inflicted.

This imagery of extinction, along with the belittling of the human powers of cognition is echoed in Nietzsche's "On Truth and Lying in a Non-Moral Sense," a work that was composed while Nietzsche was still very much a Schopenhauerian. In his classic introductory paragraph, Nietzsche gives us a charming, albeit chilling fable.

---

[9] Ibid., 584.

In some remote corner of the universe, flickering in the light of the countless solar systems into which it had been poured, there was once a planet on which clever animals invented cognition. It was the most arrogant and most mendacious minute in the "history of the world;" but a minute was all it was. After nature had drawn a few more breaths the planet froze and the clever animals had to die. [10]

Nietzsche's apocalyptic fantasy resembles Schopenhauer's, but makes special mention of "cognition" or "Erkennen." Nietzsche uses the term interchangeably with "Intellekt" and uses it to speak of the distinctly human intellect that makes up for our lack of horns, claws, or other natural protections.[11] Schopenhauer's use of the term, "Erkenntniss," or cognition, is to be contrasted with "Wissen," which is non-intuitive, abstract, and distinctly human knowledge.[12] Nietzsche's states that the idea that the intellect gives humans a special, elevated standing in the universe is absurd, since "if we could communicate with a midge, we would hear that it too floats through the air with the very same pathos, feeling that it too contains within itself the flying center of the world."[13] In this Schopenhauerian conception of world, insects claim the same position as the authors of the world as man at his most brilliant.

---

[10] Friedrich Nietzsche, "Truth and Lying in a Non-Moral Sense," *The Birth of Tragedy and Other Writings* (Cambridge: Cambridge University Press, 1999), 141.

[11] Ibid., 142.

[12] Arthur Schopenhauer, *The World as Will and Representation, Volume 1* (Cambridge: Cambridge University Press, 2010), xlix.

[13] Friedrich Nietzsche, "Truth and Lying in a Non-Moral Sense." *The Birth of Tragedy and Other Writings* (Cambridge: Cambridge University Press, 1999), 141.

Martin Heidegger would have disagreed with this judgment. While Heidegger's most famous writings on the concept of world occur in *Being and Time*, for the purposes of this piece, I believe that his 1929-30 lecture course, *Fundamental Concepts of Metaphysics*, provides a more relevant discussion, particularly in that Heidegger discusses the possibility of animal worlds. In this lecture, Heidegger tentatively defines world as "the sum total of beings accessible to man or animals alike variable as it is in range and depth of penetrability."[14] This definition seems to fall in line with that of his contemporary, Jakob von Uexküll, or even of Schopenhauer, but Heidegger does not want to fully grant animals worlds.[15] Heidegger states that the stone is world-less, man is world-forming, and the animal occupies an intermediary position of "poor in world."[16] The difference between man and animal ultimately boils down to animals not apprehending "something *as* something, something *as* a being at all."[17] While the animal possesses a world of beings, it never recognizes them as beings themselves, which Heidegger sees as a precondition for "world."[18] The animal is instead held in "captivation" by its immediate environment, a "disinhibition ring," which results in its only being able to react to that which is immediately before it.[19] The Schopenhauerian "world" appears to be merely this "disinhibition ring," while the Heideggerian world would to Schopenhauer be the solely human world of abstraction. Heidegger sees the animal as being able to act only on its

---

[14] Martin Heidegger, *The Fundamental Concepts of Metaphysics: World, Finitude, Solitude* (Bloomington: Indiana University Press, 1995), 193.

[15] Ibid., 263.

[16] Ibid., 184.

[17] Ibid., 264.

[18] Ibid., 269-270.

[19] Ibid., 271. Captivation is discussed at great length, particularly at 259-260.

drives, unlike man.[20] Schopenhauer, on the other hand, would see this as an obscuring of the drives, since man's actions are as determined as an animal's or even water in a fountain.[21]

What Heidegger adds to his conception of world, which does not contradict Schopenhauer but does surpass him, is the notion of "earth." In his "The Origin of the Work of Art," Heidegger instead asserts that the animal is world-less, but also gives world a new foundation.[22] World is a "self-opening openness" unveiled to us, while earth is perpetually concealed from us.[23] The two are inseparable but distinct. "World is grounded on earth, and earth rises up through world."[24] Earth is that from which world emerges, but which is itself always hidden. The two are perpetually in a state of "strife" but rely upon each other. World cannot be grounded without earth, and earth cannot manifest without world.[25] The world is the world for us, while the earth is always concealed.

The terminology of world and earth is picked up and expanded upon by Eugene Thacker in his book, *In the Dust of This Planet*. His use of both terms continues the traditions of Schopenhauer and Heidegger, with what we call "world" being "the world-for-us" and the earth being "the world-in-itself."[26] Thacker, however, adds another member to this now-trinity, "planet." While earth is in itself,

---

[20] Ibid., 237.

[21] Arthur Schopenhauer, *The Two Fundamental Problems of Ethics* (Cambridge: Cambridge University Press, 2009), 62-63.

[22] Martin Heidegger, "The Origin of the Work of Art," *Off the Beaten Track* (Cambridge: Cambridge University Press, 2002), 23.

[23] Ibid., 26.

[24] Ibid.

[25] Ibid., 27.

[26] Eugene Thacker, *In the Dust of This Planet: Horror of Philosophy, Volume 1* (Washington: Zero Books, 2011), 6.

planet is explicitly the "world-without-us."[27] Planet is the world that is not merely indifferent to our presence, but which exists in our complete absence. To conceive of the world as planet is to imagine an "impersonal and anonymous" world.[28] The topic of Thacker's book (and the trilogy it begins) is the "horror of philosophy," and its argument is that horror "is a non-philosophical attempt to think about the world-without-us-philosophically."[29] Thacker's project encompasses both the literary and cinematic works that we usually associate with "horror," but also philosophical works and meditations on events such as climate change.[30]

I agree with Thacker that the horror of an apocalyptic event, such as climate change, is largely this thought of the "world without us." What I want to reimagine, though, is the "planet," which is visualized as a dead world. Rather than imagining that what we are doing is killing the Earth and leaving a husk, I propose that we are simply recalibrating the Earth in such a way that it casts us aside in the same way that it did the trilobites, primitive therapsids, and non-avian dinosaurs in past extinction events. We are creating a situation in which there would still be worlds, but none of them would be human. Even though we may be asked to leave, the party of life would continue.

The visceral horror of this thought is exemplified in H.P. Lovecraft's 1936 novella, "The Shadow Out of Time." The story is of a professor who awakens to find that he has no memories of the past

---

[27] Ibid.
[28] Ibid., 7.
[29] Ibid., 9.
[30] Ibid., 4 and 9.

five years and had acted strangely during this missing time.[31] He slowly pieces together, from hallucinations, that during that lost time his body was inhabited by the consciousness of a member of the Great Race of Yith, a creature that lived in the Cretaceous period. Moreover, during that time his own mind was sent back to the creature's era, inhabited its body, and was instructed to write a history of his own age.[32] He is not the only being to be imprisoned in a Yithian body though, as there are humans from many other ages, beings from elsewhere in the solar system, and even creatures from other prehistoric races.[33] Five of his fellow inmates are "from the hardy coleopterous species immediately following mankind."[34] This is to say that our protagonist learns with full certainty that mankind will not only become extinct, but that beetles will replace us. He says that "what was hinted in the speech of post-human entities of the fate of mankind had such an effect on me that I will not set it down here," but that "after man there would be a mighty beetle civilisation [sic]."[35] In fact, he learns that ultimately it is the beetle race whose bodies his Mesozoic captors want to inhabit when their own civilization falls, but only until "earth's span closed" and they transfer their minds to "bulbous vegetable entities of Mercury."[36] The Earth would still have life-worlds upon it, since after the beetles there would be species "clinging pathetically to the cold planet and burrowing to its horror-filled core, before the utter end."[37]

---

[31] H.P. Lovecraft, "The Shadow Out of Time," *The New Annotated H.P. Lovecraft* (New York: Liveright Publishing, 2014), 714.

[32] Ibid., 738.

[33] Ibid., 739.

[34] Ibid.

[35] Ibid., 740.

[36] Ibid.

[37] Ibid.

Lovecraft's protagonist is essentially give a terminal prognosis for the human race and one that is completely out of his hands. Laird Barron's 2007 short story, "The Forest," gives mankind a similar fate, albeit one that seems to be self-inflicted. "The Forest" follows a filmmaker who is invited to a cabin in New England by a zoologist about whom he made a successful documentary years before. He finds that the zoologist is running experiments with large satellite dishes that are peculiarly pointed at the ground and is courting financiers who all appear to be close to death.[38] The impetus for these experiments is explained by the zoologist's assistant who laments that "mankind is definitely eating himself out of house and home. The beetles and cockroaches are in the direct line of succession."[39] The zoologist laments that "Man is completely and utterly alone in a sea of dust and smoke. Alone and inevitably slipping into extinction."[40] Yet while humans are creating an environment that is unfit for themselves and most of the vertebrate kin, they are opening up the world for arthropods that live deep within the ground, the "ur-Progenitors" of insects and spiders.[41] The purpose of the satellite dishes is to attempt communication with the insects before our inevitable extinction and to petition them to preserve some of us in their future kingdom. The love interest of the protagonist, a terminally ill woman, is lucky enough to be picked by them for this immortality, but a prerequisite is to be devoured by the future race. As the zoologist sadly remarks:

---

[38] Laird Barron, "The Forest," *Occultation and Other Stories* (New York: Night Shade Books, 2010), 14-17.

[39] Ibid., 17.

[40] Ibid., 26.

[41] Ibid., 26.

"Occasionally one of us, a volunteer, is permitted to cross over, to relinquish his or her flesh to the appetites of the colony and exist among them in a state of pure consciousness [...] These volunteers become the interpreters, the facilitators of communication between our species. They become undying repositories of our civilization... a civilization that shall become ancient history one day very soon."[42]

The story is asking us to imagine a means of survival that would require losing everything that we have except for our simple ability to form a world, even if it is merely a world of insects. In a way, Barron casts human beings in the same light that Lovecraft casts the Great Race of Yith – as doomed beings who are willing to undergo monstrous transformations to keep their worlds alive long after their physical extinction.

This is the point of horror often lost in discussions about anthropogenic destruction of the environment. Human beings are not so much hurting the earth in itself, an earth that has weathered numerous extinction events. Rather, we are making the earth into an earth that cannot produce the sort of worlds that we envision surviving us. Both Lovecraft and Barron give us a startling future, one in which alien and indifferent worlds exist without us. Essentially, human beings are willing the world, not to their children's children, but to insectoid and vermiform opportunists. If one merely cares about the continuation of life or the continuation of the world in a Schopenhauerian sense, such scenarios can be seen as acceptable, perhaps even fascinating. The survival of earth and planet are guaranteed long after we alter the environment to a point where it is

---

[42] Ibid., 32.

unrecognizable, and the survival of life and life-worlds is nearly as inevitable. What is not inevitable, however, is that this future earth will play hosts to worlds that are familiar to us. We, as a species, are counter-intuitively readjusting the state of the earth so that it shall not sustain our kind of life in the future. Unless we take action to maintain an earth that can sustain human worlds, then we are merely bequeathing it all to insects.

Bibliography

Barron, Laird. "The Forest" in *Occultation and Other Stories*. New York: Night Shade Books, 2010.

Heidegger, Martin. *The Fundamental Concepts of Metaphysics: World, Finitude, Solitude*. Translated by William McNeill and Nicholas Walker. Bloomington: Indiana University Press, 1995.

— "The Origin of the Work of Art." *Off the Beaten Track*. Edited and Translated by Kenneth Haynes and Julian Young. Cambridge: Cambridge University Press, 2002.

Lovecraft, H.P. "The Shadow Out of Time." *The New Annotated H.P. Lovecraft*. Edited by Leslie Klinger. New York: Liveright Publishing, 2014.

Nietzsche, Friedrich. "Truth and Lying in a Non-Moral Sense." *The Birth of Tragedy and Other Writings*. Edited by Raymond Guess and Ronald Speirs. Translated by Ronald Speirs. Cambridge: Cambridge University Press, 1999.

Schopenhauer, Arthur. "On The Will in Nature." *On the Fourfold Root of the Principle of Sufficient Reason and Other Writings*. Edited and Translated by David Cartwright, Edward Erdmann, and Christopher Janaway. Cambridge: Cambridge University Press, 2012.

— *The Two Fundamental Problems of Ethics*. Edited and Translated by Christopher Janaway. Cambridge: Cambridge University Press, 2009.

— *The World as Will and Representation, Volume 1*. Edited and Translated by Christopher Janaway, Judith Norman, and Alistair Welchman. Cambridge: Cambridge University Press,

2010.

— *The World as Will and Representation, Volume 2*. Translated by E.F.J. Payne. New York: Dover Publications, 1966.

Thacker, Eugene. *In the Dust of This Planet: Horror of Philosophy, Volume 1*. Washington: Zero Books, 2011.

Trigger

By Julie Travis

IRST, THE vandalism of the body.

A razor blade is easily obtained by levering apart a disposable razor with a penknife. Two blades are then available, although only one should be necessary. On other occasions there has been a more ritualistic element; certain music played, a clean towel laid across the bed, bandages ready. As this will be the last time, there is no need for any of these things. Left-handed, the razor is held between the thumb and forefinger on the blunt side. The blood in the veins is bubbling now, needing to be set free. So the cutting begins.

Beginning near the wrist, on the top of the right arm, the razor cuts

and cuts

and cuts

and cuts

and cuts

and cuts

and cuts.

Line after line of neat slits along the arm, up to the elbow joint. It is not a frenzied attack. It is premeditated preparation for murder. Thus, the razor does not go deep. It does not need to. Muscles will not be damaged, bones will be left unbroken. On a previous occasion an ambulanceman has described the cuts as *superficial wounds* but there is nothing insincere about them; they run deep into the psyche. As the skin knits back together and begins to heal, the wounds run deeper. As some disappear, but some do not and become scars—to itch on a sunny day and invite unwelcome, intrusive comments from strangers—the words of the ambulanceman become a sneer. *Inconsequential* wounds. Glib. Insignificant.

There is no pain. Not physical pain. Should the body and soul survive until morning (which it will not), the body would awake with the arm feeling as if it were on fire. For now it is just the relief of release, but the horror of what is being performed is not lost upon the lost soul. Blood squeezes its way out of the narrow wounds, not dramatically but in drops, and edges slowly away from each cut. At the same time the soul feels something else making its way out of the slits. Like steam from a boiling kettle, a little of the distress of the last thirty years makes its way out into the world. Usually this is enough. Having *let the Devil out*, the soul has been sated and the body collapses into sleep. But not this time. This time, this is just the beginning, the start of the end, the journey into blessed, eternal oblivion.

Should a suicide note be written? A last communication with loved ones, an attempt at an explanation for what is an inexplicable

Trigger

act to anyone who has not trodden the same path? How long should such a note be? Only an autobiography, a minute by minute account of the soul's life, every experience, every slight, every insult, every dismissal, would begin to explain the act about to be committed. More than that, the soul's observation of the world would need to be included. Each injustice to human or animal perpetrated over millennia would have to be noted. It would be polar bears starving to death, souls fleeing murderous soldiers, the terror of a lamb in an abattoir, the agony of a fox torn to shreds, the deformed bodies born to Hiroshima survivors. And more – every nightmare suffered by the soul, the fears that ghostly horsemen would gallop across the garden to the house to wreak havoc upon the family, the bullies in every corridor at school, the man who convinced the soul it was worthless and completely alone. And yet more - the soul when very young having heard a song playing on the radio, the lyrics promising that one morning the soul would awake and find the rest of family vanished during the night and gone far, far away, never to return. Deliberate abandonment, the song a warning of what was to come. Then, older, the terror of awaiting the flash of detonation, a nuclear bomb that would burn the flesh from the bones and vaporize the beautiful apple tree in the garden that had provided so much shade on sunny days, the branches friendly arms to climb upon. The soul knows that there is not enough time to write everything that should be written. Instead there is just an inadequate goodbye, the knowledge that joy will be felt now the soul has peace.

The vandalism continues. The body is cut again, on the shoulders and stomach. Blood graffiti in hidden places, a tag to say the razor was here and left its mark. The body is experiencing euphoria, the rush of endorphins in reaction to the pain it cannot feel. A small bottle is found, with the words *Inhale Me* on the label. Amyl Nitrate makes the body's head and heart race, almost to blackout, and the soul wants the heart to burst, but it does not. The soul is aware from previous attempts at oblivion that the body is incredibly strong and will not fail if poisoned by overdoses of sleeping pills or painkillers. It is possible that if every moment could be lived like this, in utter and equal distress and joy, then life could be continued, but the distress is the advancing and conquering army, and joy is always in retreat.

The soul sees its face in the mirror and decides not to vandalise its features. Too public a declaration of deviation. The body has on previous occasions walked the streets near its home, blood dripping from long sleeves that were meant to soak up and cover up the act. It is not known whether this was the soul's attempt to find help or just to see how the living live. Instead, on this last occasion, the soul has withdrawn and disconnection from the body is now complete.

Next, the destruction of the body. The soul has laboriously researched the method to be used. Each has its dangers in failure. To be paralysed or bed-bound is to submit to an endless horror. To be unable to end life cannot be allowed to happen. It has been concluded that falling from height is the preferred method. It is perfectly possible to achieve oblivion from a fall of a few feet if the body falls onto its head, but it is safer and surer to fall at least eighty-five feet onto either a hard surface or a body of water. The soul has a horror of the body being lost, even more than being abandoned, so it cannot bear the possibility of disappearing into the depths of the sea, forever, never being found, with loved ones never being sure of the soul's death, so falling into water has been ruled out. Instead, the body must fall onto a hard surface from a great height.

The location of the fall has demanded further research. The city provides many possibilities, but the soul wishes to find oblivion without observers, and the city is perpetually crowded. But the body walked past a tall building with scaffolding erected to the roof, a giant ladder a hundred feet high, and the soul realised that, should it be scaled at an early hour of the morning, the city would be quiet, and the fall could be made without witnesses. As the soul leaves the house and walks towards the tall building, the last walk it will ever experience, it wonders whether souls on approaching the gallows felt this amount of anticipation, if the screaming and roaring in the body's head was anticipation that it would all be over soon. The light rain that falls upon the body's face, the sound of the body's shoes upon the pavement, are more intense than ever before. The senses heightened to overload. Everything has become beautiful.

But how will it be to fall from such a height? How long will it take and which part of the body will reach the ground first? The soul has had visions of hitting the concrete face first; teeth smashing, jaw ripped off, the front of the body broken but the soul not only still alive but conscious, aware only of physical agony that matches, finally, the mental agony the soul has suffered. And suffering that agony for minutes or even hours before oblivion finally arrives. But there has been too much anguish. This is the end of suffering, the end the body and soul deserve, so anything other than death outright is not acceptable.

The soul passes only one other on the way to its execution. The last it will ever see. There is no temptation to confess, to embrace or say goodbye. No wise words. Nothing but silent, deafening screaming.

The scaffold – the gallows – is easy to get onto. A ladder to ground level has been left in place, so the body is able to climb up with ease. From there it is the simplest matter to climb and climb and keep climbing until the top level is reached. At the top, the final contemplation. The screaming has become unbearable, the reality of the situation making every limb of the body ache, the stomach churn and threaten vomiting, the chest pound. The body feels alive as never before, but it is no longer euphoric. It is simply a warning of how strong it is, how difficult it is to die.

The soul makes the body bend under the scaffold poles so that it is now located on the outside of the structure. And then turns it around to face the building. It is now that the soul realises that all the slights, rejections, insults and dismissals have been pieces of a jigsaw, decades in the making, that completes here, at this moment. Just before it is broken apart forever.

The body leans back as far as it can. The body's wounded arm still does not hurt. The wounds will never hurt. It feels miraculous to know this. The coming day is for other souls – it will never dawn, the sun will never be seen or felt. Birdsong and snow and the touch of a lover – the only things the soul had ever found worthwhile – will never be experienced again. But the soul has experienced them. Despite the world's best efforts, the soul has seen beauty, but it served only to make the dreadfulness worse.

All that is needed now, for blessed oblivion, is to release the hands' grip on the scaffold pole, push back and drop, head first, onto the hardness far below.

The fingers release, and release is found.

The Master Gardener

By Nicole Vasari

T HE PAINTING arrived as part of the bequest of Mrs. Constantino A. Perentis. Mrs. Perentis, known as Cathy to her friends, was a dedicated collector of a conscious, peculiar bent: mediocre 19ᵗʰ-century British art and bric-a-brac. Cathy, with her husband's wealth at her disposal, had not a single Turner or Rossetti to her name but possessed a wealth of mawkish watercolors of the Lake District and second-rate portraits of third-rate subjects. In letters to friends and art dealers, she described her collection as a deliberate affectation, an eccentricity she cultivated as carefully, and to much the same purpose, as her husband had cultivated striped orchids. To those closest to her—her brother, Henry, and her friend Ms. Unity Peterson—Cathy called her collection and the bequest an attack on good taste. It was a sentiment and a joke that I appreciated perhaps more than the board did, bound to accept all and exhibit some of her collection to secure her generous monetary bequest.

After several weeks inventorying tattered samplers and indifferently designed furniture, the joke began to wear thin even for me. I had the occasional assistance of an intern, Tamara, but I was for the most part left alone in the storage room, matching items and catalog numbers with the lawyer's inventory. There was so much of it, so many dreary little items with smudged labels, so many crates and boxes; I began to wonder if more was being brought each night, if Cathy Perentis' humor was more sadistic than I had apprehended. When I pried the lid off the long crate, #MJ885, *Mrs. Aylesly as the Muse of History,* I expected some dim, poorly proportioned aping of Reynolds.

But when the interior box was open and I pushed the packing aside, I saw it was something quite extraordinary. It was older than most of the collection, a full-length portrait in the style of Romney. It was not, I think, quite equal to Romney, but in that room, amidst the banal and desultorily made objects of Cathy's collection, it was radiant. The portrait was of a slim, lithe young man leaning an elbow on a bit of picturesquely broken Ionian column before a background of a very English park. The colors, although simple, were limpid and luminous, and the lines and forms of the composition handled with ease and nobility. In the handsome young gentleman, this confident facility had stolen some of the living subject's vitality. The remarkable eye, the face, the hand loosely clasping a book, the whole form was imbued with a force that, the longer I looked at it, the more unsettling the impression became. This was not a simple effect of precise detail, although care, inasmuch as the taste of the era dictated, had been taken, but some suggestion, some alchemy of tint and finish that made the figure look as if he might, at any moment, start up from his mysterious reverie.

There was no signature sketched among the tumbled columns or fine grass, not even a date. There was a symbol, at a stretch a highly stylized monogram, on the cover of the book the gentleman held, but I couldn't decipher even what letters it might represent. I leaned close to the painting, studying the symbol on the book and then the details of the figure. It was much more precisely detailed than I had at first thought. Beneath the smooth finish of a studied and fashionably careless genius was a meticulous detail that described both substance and sensation. By that I mean the book seemed nearly legible to me, not because I could see what was printed on the fine pages but because the essential sense of it was signaled in its shape, its color. That face—handsome, refined, but the gleam of his eye, the shade of the visions he contemplated....

I sat up. The room was buried in the labyrinth of the museum's basement storage, windowless, the climate precisely controlled and hermetically sealed from the outside world. I felt dazed and cramped, and I began to fumble for my phone to check the time. I stopped, suddenly certain that I did not want to know how much time had passed. I pushed the packing back in the box, set the lid on it, clumsily gathered up my things, and left.

The corridors were quiet, the doors to offices shut, and when I reached the upper levels I saw that it was quickly growing dark. I had not yet stopped for lunch when I opened #MJ885. It was now after seven.

It was unsettling, annoying, to have lost so much time but it didn't strike me as uncanny, and I returned to work in the morning with no presentiment of trouble. But there were voicemails on my office phone, so rarely used it was thick with dust, and a couriered envelope from a law firm waiting for me on my desk.

I ignored the phone and opened the envelope. Inside was a letter addressed to me, not the museum, on behalf of Mr. Henry Spinther, the brother of Mrs. Catherine Perentis. Mr. Spinther, via his lawyer, demanded the return of item #P777, *Portrait of a Gentleman: The Master Gardener,* immediately, on pain of, and etc.

I knew instantly what Mr. Spinther so desperately wanted. What else among his sister's tiresome jokes would be worth the trouble of paying his lawyer? As I read the letter over again, I realized, to my surprise, that I was jealous of his claim on the portrait, that what I scrutinized each line for was some suggestion that his claim was illegitimate. I was resolved, immediately and spitefully, to thwart or at least stall his repossession of the portrait. There was no #P777 on the list and nothing to prove that the portrait I'd found last night was it. But of course, the painting wasn't mine to withhold or return, and I dutifully sent Tamara to take the letter to the director.

I descended to the storage room and the crates and boxes still to be accounted for and sorted. I was aware of the contested portrait's precise location and, even as I cataloged inept watercolors of flowers and still lifes of dead animals, I recalled it in exact detail. There was more to be seen: I desired nothing more than to lift the lid of the box and sweep aside the packing and gaze and gaze on each detail, each sensation as it was revealed to me, beyond the merely physical of form and color, the handsome face and the hazy vista of the heavenly green park, to the thoughts that drew him away from his book, the invisible secret that transfixed him.

But I knew, in some superstitious, sympathetic way, that if I so much as cracked the lid, Mr. Spinther, a bloodless mummy connected only tenuously to the world, would know.

Late in the day, Tamara knocked on the door and hovered uneasily on the threshold. She eyed the boxes and official forms choking the room, dreading, I knew, that I'd ask her to help. She told me that the director had reviewed the copies of the lists and forms delivered to our lawyers and, failing to find a #P777, had asked our lawyers to contact Mr. Spinther's.

"So who is he?" Tamara leaned against the door, growing confident that I wouldn't ask for her help. "Weird name."

I shut a bit of clumsy sampler back in its box, probably to never see light again. "Mrs. Perentis' brother. And it's Roman, isn't it?"

"Is it? What is?"

"An actor. Or a chariot racer?" I brushed my hands off and folded my arms. "There was a consul named Spinther, too, wasn't there? A Cornelia. Is that right?"

She laughed nervously. "I have no idea. How do you know that? Roman consuls? I thought you did European art."

"I like to read."

"No kidding." She surveyed the room with distasteful sympathy. "Hey. Do you want to run out for a coffee?"

"No, I'm fine," I said too quickly.

"You sure? You're not—" She floundered, visibly uncomfortable, "lonely or something down here?"

"Not at all," I said, astonished and a little touched by her concern. "We all work alone a lot."

"Yeah, I guess." She drew her cardigan over her chest and canvassed the room with another uneasy, distasteful look. "It's just this stuff, I guess. It's like... My auntie used to drag me to estate sales when I was a kid. The rich people ones, you know, big houses on the lake. It was so sad. You know how shabby some of them are really, an old person living in one or two rooms, all the other rooms full of old furniture and boxes of stuff no one's looked at for years. And then they die and there's the estate sale people all over the place and all that weird junk spread out everywhere. The Perentis stuff reminds me of that."

I laughed. "Don't be so hard on it! It'll grow on you when it's in the galleries."

Tamara made a face. "It's creepy."

"It's not the creepiest thing here."

"It's depressing."

"Find something to do," I warned her, "or I'll find something to keep you busy."

For the next several days, there were no further letters or calls for me. Mr. Spinther's lawyer was unable to produce a description of the painting beyond the title, not even the dimensions or medium, and we began to gently insist that the painting was, perhaps, mislaid in storage somewhere else. In my brief conversations with the director, I noticed something like Tamara's reluctance on the topic. It was not, I discovered, an exceptional sentiment: no one liked the Perentis collection. Of course they didn't—I didn't, really. The objects, aside from the portrait that only I had seen, were uninteresting and homely; selecting even those few items we were bound to display would not be an enviable task. It was a little demeaning to have to accept money with such unappealing conditions and disheartening to know that the institution, in fact, needed the money that badly. But the general antipathy had almost nothing to do with resentment of the terms. It was a simple and instinctive revulsion for the objects themselves or rather for the grouped mass of them.

The objects alone, interestingly, were at least indifferently received. I brought a portrait of a girl on porcelain up, as an experiment, and if it was not admired it was far from detested. So it was something else: the sheer clutter of pointless human endeavor the mass of them represented, the ubiquity of mediocrity. Or perhaps, nothing so apparent. That uneasy sentiment was not marked from the beginning, I thought, and, moving mechanically through the list, I wondered, half-seriously, if it was really one particular object that, without them ever seeing it, had begun to taint the others as soon as I opened the box.

But was there anything malignant about the portrait? Enough time had passed that I wasn't sure. Was there something cruel in the face, something unpleasant in the mild English park, something distasteful just visible on the fine pages of the book he held? I hesitated to look again; but as the details faded and Mr. Spinther disappeared behind his befuddled lawyer, it seemed a little absurd that I'd been afraid he would catch the subtle vibrations of the portrait breathing free air.

Of course, I couldn't resist.

I slid the lid of the crate aside. I had the sudden sensation of being wrenched upward, sickeningly lightheaded, and my vision dimmed and narrowed to only what was directly in front of me. That was now at a dizzy perspective, withdrawing further and further from me as if I was being drawn toward the ceiling which in turn receded higher and higher. There was a muffled pop and hiss in my ears as if I were in a poorly pressurized plane.

Then I was clutching the edge of the crate, slumped forward, almost fainting on the portrait. That elegant, beautiful painted face came back into focus below me, the soft mouth and the diabolical eye. It would have been very easy to brush my swoon off as something completely natural; I often got so absorbed I forgot to eat. But I knew, with complete certainty, that something else had happened, something had passed through me, come near me. I was afraid— naturally, I was afraid. I was alone, I was doing something I knew to be wrong from a strictly legal and professional sense, and something had happened. But I was also excited: *something had happened,* something I had perhaps always been looking for, waiting for, expecting. There was something written in the book he clasped, and I would read it.

But I was also certain that Mr. Spinther, that grotesque mummy, fount of dust, possessive of the last scraps of his life and inheritance, had caught that: no subtle vibration but a thunderclap striking his ear.

When I unlocked my office door the next morning there was someone already there. No—that's not what I thought at first. I thought it was a shadow falling across my desk, and then I thought it was a mannequin.

"Who the hell are you?" I had one hand on the door. I was ready to slam it shut and lock him in. I was breathless and shaking, my heart pounding so hard each beat was almost painful. I was terrified but also furious.

"I thought it would be best if I visited in person." He smiled and held out his hand. "Henry Spinther. I believe you've heard of me?"

"Yes." Whatever had frightened me vanished like a trick of the eye, and I was only irritated and wary. "From your lawyer."

He laughed as if I'd mentioned a mutual but tiresome friend. "Ah, yes."

"You're Henry Spinther?"

He nodded. "Yes. Absolutely."

"Mrs. Perentis' brother?" I looked him up and down, incredulous. He couldn't have been older than me, rather eccentrically but expensively dressed. This was not the powdered mummy, the ancient, Cathy's older brother. I tried to recall whether her obituary had mentioned his age or if there was any indication in her letters, but I could seize on nothing solid.

He was nodding excitedly, as if I was saying something he was caught up in. "Yes! Yes!"

The door creaked, and I caught myself on the sound. "Mr. Spinther—"

"Hal, please."

"Mr. Spinther, I don't think it's advisable for me to speak to you. Please direct any further questions or request through our lawyers—"

"Oh no!" He laughed. "You misunderstand. I'm not here to accuse. That's settled. The portrait isn't here. Isn't that what you said?" There was something unpleasantly keen and droll in his eye. "No, I'm hoping you can help me."

"What on earth?" I had the intense and intensely unpleasant conviction that two different conversations were happening, and however bizarre and inappropriate the one we carried on in the solid space of my office was, the other, which no one passing by could have heard, was worse. He spoke of something *contrary*, something impermissible or forbidden, and the alien vibration of that other voice sounded as from a cavern. "What are you talking about?"

"I'd like you to help me find the portrait. You've read Cathy's letters. You know her collection." He tilted his head, curled his lip between his teeth, and gazed at the corner of the ceiling with the rapt, blankly curious stare of a cat. "It was her joke. It was her humor. No one else would get it."

"I don't think I do."

"You do. And if she mislaid the portrait, it was a joke, too. Do you see?" He looked at me appealingly; he expected me to agree. "She left it to me. It's important that I find it."

"You're her brother?" I asked again.

"Well." He laughed and rolled his shoulders in a charming shrug. "You're the expert."

"Mr. Spinther," I stepped back. "I understand you want to recover your property. I completely sympathize, but you must understand that you cannot approach me and ask for my help this way. It's not appropriate. You'll have to go through our lawyers. I'm sorry."

"Ah." He should have been downcast, but his face was lit with a rather ghoulish excitement as if this was actually what he wanted. "Yes. Of course."

"You'll have to leave."

I had stepped back to make room for him to pass, but the corridor was narrow, and he was quite close to me for a moment. He looked down at me as he passed; there was a genuine smile on his face, louche, a little weary, humorous, and I had the sensation that I was looking at someone else entirely, that he was not Cathy's brother. Then he moved away, and I was merely annoyed at the scene and the prospect of informing the director.

A little while later, Tamara tapped at my open door.

"Yes?"

"I just…" She had an odd look on her face, as if she'd seen something shocking and unpleasant. "I was just…"

"Yes?"

She looked at me so searchingly it was almost rude. "I just saw your brother. On the stairs," she said. "I mean, I thought it was you, I really did. I looked like an idiot chasing him down. Is he—why is he—?"

"I don't have a brother."

"Yes—I saw him. Who was it?" She sounded angry. "Then who was it? Your cousin? I thought it was you."

"No. I don't have a brother. None of my cousins are here. What's the matter?"

"I thought it was you." She said, accusatory but puzzled. "I swear. He has to be— Who was up here?"

"No one!" The lie came off poorly. "It's nothing, Tamara. I'm about to go up to the director's office. I can't tell you before I tell her. Don't say anything until you hear about it from someone else, okay?"

"What the fuck?" Her eyes were wide. "Who the hell was that?"

"Listen—wait—please don't repeat this—*wait*. I'm on my way to talk to the director right now. It was Henry Spinther."

She blinked, then stepped back. "It was not," she said angrily. "I thought it was you."

"Tamara."

She took another step back, out of the door. "I thought it was you."

It wasn't until the next day that Tamara would speak to or even be in the same room as me. She was sheepish and apologetic about her aversion and unable to explain it. She'd seen me, she said, coming down the stairs, and she had rushed after me to share some throwaway office gossip. She reached the foot of the stairs just as the person she thought was me reached the bottom, and it was then that she realized her mistake. There was something obscurely shocking, to both of us, about the confusion, something both frightening and insulting.

Henry Spinther, of course, looked nothing like me, and there was not the remotest chance anyone could have mistaken us. Tamara couldn't describe the points of resemblance, but neither could she disavow that she had seen them, no matter how much I suspect she would have liked to.

The director called me into her office that afternoon and explained that I should make time in my schedule to help Mr. Spinther. There was, it seemed, no legal concern, and Mr. Spinther was supposed to be very rich and very generous to his benefactors. I asked her to relay our decision through the lawyers and left.

Although he had been informed that he had permission to make use of my expertise, Mr. Spinther thankfully did not appear for nearly a week. I continued sorting the Perentis collection. I pushed the box with the portrait into a far corner, as near to out of sight as possible. I still felt its presence, as if it stirred toward sentience like a sleeper. But I was convinced that if I listened to it, if I woke it again, I would find Henry Spinther lounging against my desk. He might come back regardless but I bargained for as much time as possible. In that small span of time I held, I studied the public record of Cathy's brother.

Cathy was born in 1920. If Henry was decades younger than her, it was remotely, improbably, possible that they shared the same father. However, the record of their correspondence dated back to her marriage in 1938—and she clearly confided in a grown, worldly man. Henry's birth certificate bore out the impression: he was born in

1918. The man I'd spoken to in my officer could not possibly be 100 years old. My first, irrational thought was that by some unknown means he concealed his age and that this was why I'd had the strange impression that I was looking at someone else. It was the mere suggestion of that means that struck me as horrible, to have been alone in a room with someone such as that. By the end of the week I'd located Henry Spinther's death certificate: He'd been stabbed to death in a bar in 1946. The murder had made the papers, where a grainy image of Henry Spinther's rather blandly handsome face stared mildly from beneath a lurid headline.

It was not the man who'd come to my office.

And yet—Cathy had continued to write to him and he to her for years afterward. I had the letters, filed and cataloged, and when I dug them out and held them in my hand I had the sickening sense of the joints of the world slipping. Who was he? Who had she spoken to in such unwaveringly intimate tones over those decades?

He was there in the morning, waiting patiently in the lobby. He'd come through the front door and spoken to the guard and waited in the lobby when they told him to do so. There was something unpleasantly pointed about it, some obvious show; he could have gone into my locked office as he had before and by choosing not to he reminded me that he might, next time, choose otherwise. He followed me up the stairs as if he'd never been there before.

"I'm so glad you can help me," he said when I let him into my office. "I know you're exactly the person I need."

I left the door open and walked behind my desk. "I'm not sure I am, actually."

He didn't answer; he turned slightly to read the titles of the books piled on my shelf. How could Tamara have mistaken him for me?

75

There was something infuriating and offensive in the thought. We were nothing alike. In fact, he looked like... And I could not think of what he looked like. He stood in front of me, and I was completely unsure of his appearance. I could not have described him in even the vaguest terms. The sense of familiarity was almost overwhelming but evaded me as completely as his appearance did. He looked as little like Cathy's brother as he did me, but what did he look like? I saw, surely, the space he occupied, I saw the lift of his eyebrow and the curve of his mouth. I saw that, but what it amounted to, the complete picture, would not assemble. It was like trying to recall someone I had met years ago: the distinct memory of their left eye, the texture of their hair, but the whole blurred and lost.

"Who..." I hadn't meant to speak. My voice was strained, pressed down to the strangled whisper of a nightmare. The sound startled me.

"Yes?"

"Who...." I struggled to stop myself from saying what I meant. "Who is the portrait of? Do you know? That might help."

"Who is it of?" he repeated vaguely. "Who? The gardener?"

"The gentleman. In the painting."

Henry Spinther—not Cathy's brother—sighed deeply. "He looked after the Casserattis' garden when he went into exile in Italy. Imagine! Exile in Italy. I think you'd be happy to be exiled to Italy, wouldn't you?"

"Do you know the name of the man in the portrait?" I don't know why I asked. It was, I think, that I wanted to carry on as best as I could. I had ruled out the possibility of telling the director what I'd learned. I was compromised, after all, and if I encouraged an investigation it would inevitably come to light that I had lied.

"Fonthill," he sighed. "William Silas Fonthill."

"Oh." I wrote the name on the back of a brochure. "And the artist?"

"I'm afraid that doesn't matter," he said sadly. "It doesn't signify—not in the least, does it?"

"It would to me."

He looked up. It was beyond unpleasant to meet his eyes—vivid, almost luminous eyes—but what did they look like? What was their color or shape? "Of course it would," he said, and I had again that sensation of a second, appalling conversation being carried on simultaneously.

"It would be helpful." I was defending myself not from an accusation—he knew, I realized, that I was lying—but from some inquiry. And I did a poor job of it. "Their style... it can help us to identify the painting when we find it."

"Ah." He sighed again. "I'm afraid I simply don't know. Do you think I could have a look through Cathy's old things? I might spot something that will be helpful."

"No." He grinned at my blunt refusal, a wide, wicked expression. "Absolutely not. I mean... we don't let people down there. You need permission, specific permission. There have been thefts. In the past."

"Thefts." His eyes almost closed in satisfaction. "Oh, of course."

He stayed for half an hour, said nothing more of consequence—although that unsettling, silent dialogue continued—then left.

William Silas Fonthill was a minor footnote in a family of diluted aristocracy but immense wealth. He was mentioned in the correspondence of both Horace Walpole and William Beckford, who referred to him as "singularly vicious," but Fonthill's correspondence with either gentlemen appeared to be lost or overlooked in collections. Fonthill's younger sister became a countess, and in her rather dry memoirs mentioned only that her brother William had fallen into "bad practices and unorthodoxy," and perhaps financial and sexual scandal, and was forced to flee to Italy where he was taken in by his friends, the Casserattis, and not heard from again. An afternoon struggling through Luchino Casseratti's correspondence yielded nothing, not even a mention that he knew Fonthill. Exhausted and defeated by failure and Luchino's idiosyncratic Italian, I leaned back in the chair in my office and closed my eyes.

It was easy to draw up the perfect image of the portrait. Were those the signs of vice and cruelty in the depth of his eyes, the set of his mouth? Were those picturesque ruins his fortune and name? What secrets did he clasp in that book, what closely traced symbols covered the binding? The sense of his presence was overwhelming. It was as if I stood in the grand ruin of a Mannerist garden and he spoke—but, because it was a dream, in neither English nor Italian, not even French or Latin—softly and quickly so that, whatever language he spoke, it sounded like distant weather or the ambient drone of summer in that grand Italian garden.

I felt a shadow fall across my face like a hand. I opened my eyes, absolutely awake but my ears still ringing with that chattering drone, to see Henry Spinther. I almost caught him then, I almost saw him, but I flinched back instinctively.

"Are you very busy?" he asked politely, and then, boldly ironic: "Have you found anything?"

"Who..." I caught myself. "Who sent you up?"

78

"I've been doing my own research," he said. There was no other chair in my office so he sat, without invitation or the pretense of apology, on the edge of my desk. "I talked to Cathy's maids. They said they remembered the portrait but she'd had it put away years ago."

"You never noticed?"

"Yes?"

I pushed my chair back and stood, sorting through the papers and books on my desk and moving carefully away from him. "You didn't notice when she had it moved? I thought the two of you were close."

He laughed. "You must know Cathy so well by now."

"But you knew her better. Aren't you her brother?"

He glanced down then raised his eyes and fixed me with a look of such satisfaction, such monstrous repletion and excitement. "Ah... am I?"

"Aren't you?"

"Aren't I...? Something like that?" He pursed his lips thoughtfully. "That's how it's said, isn't it?" He laughed lightly, a rill of gentle delight and wonder. "Yes, she would say that. She did say that."

"Did you? Are you, really?"

"But it's all settled." There was again that nauseating incongruity, the conviction that another conversation was taking place and his reactions, the smile, the delighted laugh, the way he narrowed his eyes, were in response to what was said in that other, silent discourse. "Does it matter to you?"

"No." I had begun to move slowly around the desk but kept the width of the office between us. I checked papers and books, put things away, watered the plants, all in a careful, almost unconscious circuit toward the door. "It doesn't."

"My sister, then. My aunt. A cousin. My mother."

"I don't care," I said. I was close to the door; I could see his shadow against the corner of my eye. "It really doesn't matter to me."

"I'd like to see her collection," he said.

"Out of the question." My hand was on the door. "I'm sorry, but I told you."

He was standing in front of me, looking down, and he touched my wrist. "I know you're lying," he said as if he regretted having to be so blunt. "I know you lied."

I had once walked into a store as it was being robbed and managed to back out and disappear around the corner into the busy shuffle of pedestrian traffic before anyone quite realized I'd interrupted the crime. I had been afraid for my life, a deeply primitive fear. I responded in a purely instinctive, animal way, and it was the sudden and unadorned revelation that what I had previously considered my conscious, human mind was merely a gloss on the truth that left me shaken for months after. This was worse because the threat implied was not simply—was not at all—physical.

"You're not her brother."

"It's here, isn't it? If they went right now and searched, they'd find it, and then it wouldn't matter who I am." He hadn't moved, but he was closer, hanging over me. "It's here—it's there. Take me now."

I led him down and down and through the corridors and connecting rooms of the basement to the storage room where Cathy Perentis' collection remained barely half-cataloged. Then he led me, still holding my wrist but indifferently as if he'd forgotten I was there, to the long box that held the portrait. He dropped my arm, but I was held as surely as he was, snared by those same cobweb strands that had drawn him here. He fell to his knees and pushed the lid away and, trembling violently, he clawed the packing aside.

He made a sound of pain when he saw the portrait, a short, sharp noise as if he'd received a sudden blow. He touched the painted face, the ruined columns, the fine hand that held the book that fell open under his shaking fingers, the closely written pages rattling as they turned.

And then I was alone in the room, surrounded by the unlovely remnants of a joke.

Henry Spinther was never heard from again. The money he had promised the museum in exchange for my assistance was, I learned later, transferred through his lawyers, who themselves disappeared after the transaction. I eventually finished cataloging the collection and selected a few of the more droll items for display. The portrait was not one of them.

I didn't return to the storage room for two weeks. When I did, I crept up to the portrait, my face averted, and heaved the lid back on the box without looking at it. I left it that way, untouched, sealed in darkness, for a month before I dared look at it again. In that time a change had come over the portrait. That wonderful vitality was gone, and even the exquisite finesse of the technique had vanished. There was something rather coarse and pedestrian about the painting. In the weeks that followed, it's deterioration progressed. The varnish, formerly in good condition, cracked like a shattered pane of glass, and the paint began to flake off. In a few months, the wonderful portrait was so much insipidly colored dust on frayed canvas.

Now, as I sit alone in that storage room where the watercolors and samplers and curtains will be shut away for as good as forever, I can place at last who Henry Spinther looked so much like. He had the same face as the portrait's. He looked nothing like me. No one could have possibly mistaken us.

Parasitic Castration

By Amelia Gorman

Sacculina, darling barnacle,
hub of reconnected wires in the core
of a crab, turning both gametes to melting
wax and rising nurture up the gorge
limbs lost
molting stopped
only slick
smooth flesh
a plastic
doll of a crab
Flat and feminine now, it dowses
its one-handed scuttle to the water

where it swishes baby barnacles
into the tide like its own
So where is the parasite
who will push the nurture back in me?
Grubs I can stick under my thighs,
I force my eyes under wasp speckled lights
flex my elbows in the algae hoping
little cysts will migrate for them
suck on my armpits, my tongue, my neck
I spoon dirty river into my mouth
and slog in hookwormed soil up to my knees
My skeleton is full grown, indoors
and I could never replace my parts
But I could stand in some wet patch
waving splayed hands through the water, remembering
what it was like to want this

Title: The Town Manager
Artist: Serhiy Krykun

The November House

By Charles Wilkinson

M R. PLANT could no long recall why he was living in a tall brick house in the District. Wherever he'd been previously must have proved in some respects unsatisfactory. Yet it was only since his arrival that his mouth had become smaller. Although to be accurate, his lips were contracting; the space of the interior, as he discovered by running his tongue over his teeth and palate, remained approximately the same. In the mornings, when he peered into the mirror, his mouth resembled a puffer fish's. For a man in late middle age, his skin, especially around the cheeks, was oddly smooth; no smile lines, but then he had never been given to good humour - nor even faint cordiality. Was he speaking to fewer people, so the muscles around the mouth received less exercise? At his previous address there'd been a number of people he'd been obliged to speak to, even though he'd disliked their company. He knew no one in the District. His conversations were limited to the briefest exchanges with the owner of the General Store and a weekly argument with the imbecile who drove the delivery van for Ferryman's Wines & Spirits.

Outside, a grey November sky pressed down on a row of buildings in shabby red brick, long ago converted from Victorian manufactories to residential use. Mr. Plant went over to the window. The doors and lintels in the dwellings opposite were in poor repair. Most of the roofs were flat, in keeping with an industrial past. Although the District had resisted gentrification, there was one house with a pitched roof, a Georgian fanlight and a dressed stone façade, the only house in the street with aspirations to elegance. It must once have been the home of a manager or overseer. In spite of his ankle length overcoat, Mr. Plant shivered. The ceilings on the ground floor were high; the glass in the sash window thin. Bare wood showed through paint on the window frames. He smiled experimentally at a pigeon; a flash of pain on his upper lip. When was the last time he'd spoken to anyone? Two days ago – or perhaps three – he'd visited the General Store. And since then? Nothing and nobody.

As he moved towards the telephone, his knees cracked and popped. He fumbled the receiver with his thick, woolen gloves. A number had been written on a small sheet on the table. He dialed. In the grate, there was no more than the faint, orange suggestion of a flame and ash.

"Plant speaking,' he said. "I just wanted to say I haven't given up."

There was a click and then silence.

"I'm still committed to the project. I know I haven't made any headway on it for almost two months now. The fact of the matter is I can't get up the stairs. This November cold has got into my bones. When the weather is warmer, I promise I'll start work again."

No reply. Yet he'd a decided sense of a process in progress at the other end of the line. Were his words being recorded?

Something was tickling his upper lip.

"I won't make any excuses, but the pain is insufferable. It's not just in my knees, but in my hands and back as well. Even if I managed to get up the stairs, I couldn't come down again. But in the summer I'll reach the patch of grass by the canal. I'll start once I've had some sun on my body."

A streak of wetness was working its way down his chin. He took off one of his gloves and wiped his face. Blood from the crack in his upper lip. He put the receiver down and began to dab at himself with a grey handkerchief. In this cold it will soon clot, he thought.

Plant was dozing when the bell rang. For once, he had slept well on the sofa. Draping an overcoat on top of the blankets had helped. Part of the technique was not to move too much during the night but to burrow into the cushions, imagine oneself as gone to earth. He was more or less clothed; the previous night he'd failed to undress fully. The brown van parked outside had the words Ferryman's Fine Wines & Spirits (Est. 1666) on the side in Gothic red letters. There was no address or telephone number. A conversation would be impossible to avoid. Plant moistened his upper lip to prevent the crack reopening.

He drew back three bolts and unlocked the front door. The

same as last week: a bald, clean-shaven man wearing a tweed jacket over blue overalls. He was holding a cardboard box.

"If you'll just stand aside, sir, I'll take the delivery down to the cellar if you've no need of it."

"I thought I made it clear last time that you were to cancel the order, which was never made by me, as you well know."

"Come on, sir, we've been through all this."

"Well, let's go through it again, shall we?"

The man put down the cardboard box on the front steps and rubbed his arms. "Be reasonable. It's not as if you're paying for this lot, is it? Why not let me put it in the cellar as we agreed. After all, you don't go down there, do you? On account of your disabilities."

"I don't drink alcohol. Find out who is sending these compulsory gifts and tell them that their generosity must stop."

The man made a pantomime of taking out the delivery note, as if to check the precise wording; his lips twisted in the pedantic smirk of a solicitor's clerk. "Now strictly speaking, sir. There is no personal involvement on the part of any individual whatsoever. The deliveries come with the property, so to speak, and you, being the current leaseholder, are obligated to accept them. In short, to be brief, and to put it in as few words as I am able, sir: the delivery is to the house and not the resident therein."

"Take it away and don't come back."

The man's features hardened as he glared at Plant. "What's to be delivered is to be delivered," he said.

"Not here."

"They've got another set."

"A set of what?"

"Keys, of course. To all your doors. Take it from me, sir; you'd be best off letting me in now. The other fellow wouldn't like it if he has to come out."

A few minutes later, once the cardboard box was in the cellar and the van had been driven away down the street, Mr. Plant took out the business card he had insisted on being given in return for allowing the man into the house:

Ferryman & Co, Purveyors of Fine Wines
Spirits & Home-brewed Ales, Stouts
& Corkers since 1666
Chairman: C. Ferryman, Esq.

Still no address, no number. Perhaps if he were to venture out he would find a telephone book, but he couldn't recall seeing one of the red boxes in the area. He went over to the window. The sky was icy grey; no sign of the pigeons he sometimes glimpsed flitting from chimney pot to chimney pot or pecking around in the street. Perhaps they had frozen to their nests. I'm being simple-minded, he thought.

Directory enquiries. He went over to the phone.

"Please put me through to Ferryman & Co."

"Have you got the first line of the address?"

"No, unfortunately not. But they're wine merchants. Perhaps they're listed in the business section."

"That's where …ah here they are … oh, I'm afraid I can't do that; I'm not allowed to disclose the number."

"Why? Are they ex-directory."

"Not exactly. It's only possible to contact them if you are in another region."

Dark before five o'clock, and no food in the house. Mr. Plant struggled into the overcoat that he wore on top of the trench coat that he no longer took off, at least not until the height of summer. Then he put on a fur hat, purchased on a visit to the Arctic Circle many years before. His four scarves covered his chest and the lower half of his face. Having unbolted the front door, he winced as he went down three stone steps and into the street. It'll be easier now you're on the flat, he thought; yet still the pain flared with every pace. His knees cracked antiphonally. A sudden drop in temperature had powdered the pavement with frost. As always, there were no lights on in the overseer's house. Perhaps it had been ripped apart inside: the period fire places and even the decorative plasterwork long since removed; the place now too dilapidated for a squat. Only the elegant proportions of the façade hinted at a lost authority.

The bow windows of the Bag of Nails were illuminated by a brassy, hospitable glow. Mr. Plant caught a glimpse of wooden paneling, the chestnut patina of a leather sofa, a copper warming pan on a wall. Even the counter had a curious sparkle, although there was only one customer, who stood at the head of the horseshoe-shaped bar, where a hatch might once have been when the pub was divided: the lounge on the left, the right-hand side with a bare floor covered in sawdust.

In spite of the cold, Mr. Plant stopped to watch. The solitary drinker raised his gleaming, amber pint to his lips at exact intervals, appearing to drink the same quantity each time. Apart from the mechanical regularity with which he drank, he was quite still; his left hand, flat and unmoving, supported him as he leant forward on the bar. He'd grey hair, yellow over the ears. There was a faint patch of gold on one of his splayed fingers. A signet ring? The barman refilling his pint was young with a smooth face and a pear-shaped body surmounted by a tiny head, slightly wider at the bottom than at the top of his prematurely balding head. He had a smooth forehead and a slick black widow's peak. Mr. Plant had never passed the pub without seeing the two men, although at no point had there been the slightest indication of a conversation or even any sign of money being exchanged. It was as though they were stuck in something close to a tableau, where only a few repetitive movements were permitted. Just as he was about to move, Mr. Plant noticed, for the first time, the name of the brewer on the sign over the door: *Ferryman's Fine Ales & Stouts.*

The General Store was on a corner at the end of the street. A narrow shop with a tall ceiling, it was inadequately lit, its many shelves so packed with produce that Mr. Plant frequently found it necessary to ask for assistance. A bell rang, and the Asian man who ran it emerged from a gloomy recess at the back.

"Evening, Boss."

Mr. Plant placed his order and watched as his small bag was stacked with essentials. He never ordered too much. He'd grown weaker, and his hands were gnarled and inflamed, just capable of grasping the handle.

"Tell me, you don't happen to know the name of the man who is always drinking in the Bag of Nails?"

"Nah, don't go in there, Boss. I don't drink alcohol, me."

"But you must have seen him, surely?"

"Yeah, always there, inhe? But like I say, I've never met the man. Different circles, know what I mean?"

"Even so, you must have heard something. He has to be famous in the District."

"In the Bag of Nails, perhaps. But I don't ask no questions about what goes on in that place, Boss."

"But some of your customers must have mentioned him."

The Asian man glanced around his store. Apart from Plant, there was no one present. He leant forward, lowering his voice as he spoke: "They say he's the sort of bloke who knows everything. Always got a story to tell. Doesn't like to be interrupted, if you know what I mean. After a while, all the locals stopped coming in."

"I'm surprised the landlord didn't bar him."

"They say the man's a Ferryman. Family member, know what I mean? Anyway the landlord's not bothered. On account of his disability."

The shop bell rang, and the Asian man moved away to serve two new customers. What disability? Plant wondered, as he left the shop. The barman did have a strangely shaped head. Was he also the landlord?

At breakfast, Mr. Plant had to slice his toast into small sections. His mouth had narrowed to an aperture less than a third of its normal width. That this condition was a medical one and not simply a by-product of natural taciturnity now seemed apparent. Even though he'd spent an hour on mouth exercises the previous night, the benefits were short lived. At first, when he'd woken up, he thought the lower half of his face had sealed over. It took him some time to work his way back inside with his little finger. Although towards the end of the meal, he'd managed to extend his mouth sufficiently to pop in a small sausage, his lips then snapped back into place like a rubber band. He was not registered with a doctor in the District; indeed, now that he considered it, he was certain he had not sought medical assistance of any kind for many years. The skin that covered part of his mouth was not especially thick. Was remedial action with a kitchen knife the way forward? It would be foolish to risk infection from an open wound. He recalled that cotton wool, bandages and antiseptic creams were in a cabinet on the second floor. If he somehow managed to get upstairs, he would also be able to spend time on his project. An ascent would be painful and time-consuming, but now he had two reasons for making it.

Not long after he had managed to drag himself up the first four steps, the bell rang. He had forgotten it was delivery day. It had taken him almost twenty minutes to limp and crawl as far as he had up the staircase. Surrendering his hard-won position to take a delivery that he'd neither ordered nor needed was out of the question. The bell rang again, five times in sharp succession. The noise drove him one step higher.

"Open up!" a voice, immediately recognizable as that of the bald man, screamed. "I can hear you shuffling about in there."

Plant lowered himself carefully. He would simply keep quiet for minute or two. No doubt the fool would give up and go away.

A furious rattling of the handle; the sound of first a closed and then an open hand hammering on the door. "A delivery from Ferryman and Co to be made to this house today or face the consequences!"

And now a finger was pressed down hard on the bell; the other hand thudded on the door as if to break it down. Would the bolts hold?

"Go away!" Plant screamed. "Kindly tell your superiors that I will not accept any further deliveries."

"Unlock the door. Then we can discuss this."

"No deliveries ... not today ... nor on any other day."

"The decision's not yours to make. Not rightly."

"I've nothing further to add."

"Do you want him to come round then? I can't believe that."

"I've no idea who *he* is. Stop issuing barely intelligible threats and go about your business."

"He may not come today ... or even tomorrow. But he'll be here. By the end of the week at the very latest."

Footsteps. The sound of the van being driven away. Gratitude brought him to his feet; then he registered the full extent of the pain, the molten lava rising beneath the kneecaps and searing down his left leg. He forced himself up four more stairs. There was every chance of reaching the landing within the next half hour.

When he'd last visited it, his studio had been filled with early August gold. Perhaps viewing what he'd done in winter light would suggest a way forward. He might even make a few alterations, but there was no source of heat in the house, apart from the gas ring and the fire on the ground floor. Already he could feel the swelling in his finger joints. It would be foolish to risk making a mistake when his hands were in such poor condition.

He reached the bathroom. The mirror was well positioned and he could examine his mouth. A membrane formed of pale whitish skin strengthened with gristle covered the left side. His lips on the right appeared narrower than he recalled. The corner of the mouth was latticed with flesh. A quick examination of the medicine cabinet revealed he was correct in assuming he'd find cotton wool and antiseptics. But he'd forgotten to bring the kitchen knife. He found a pair of nail scissor and tried to make a few adjustments to the place where the skin was least well established; even the thinnest strand had a rubbery resilience. When tested, the blades proved blunt

He made his way down the corridor and into the studio. His project, a structure of stone and metal that he came to refer to as "the built companion," stood on a plinth in the middle of the room. The bodywork was predominantly steel; the head marble. The features of the upper half of the face were refined and delicate, suggesting a beauty of mind as well as form; the lower half of the head consisted of jagged stone, chipped and chiseled until there was no longer sufficient material to create a convincing jaw line.

He recalled how he had been unable to create a pair of lips that he'd wished to kiss. For the first time, he understood he'd ruined the marble; only by ordering another block would he be able to complete "the built companion." Involuntarily, he put a hand to his mouth and at once a silent question came to him with an almost audible force: *If you can no longer kiss, why eat?*

Plant spent the night in his bedroom, his first there for many months. No matter how many blankets he'd piled up, he'd been unable to keep out the cold. As soon as he felt strong enough, he would make the descent. But as he was upstairs there were a few things he must do. Once in the bathroom, he took out cotton wool, plasters and a tube of antiseptic cream, all of which he put into a pocket of his inner overcoat. He went into the landing, picked up a receiver and pressed the key for the answer phone.

You have three messages.

He pressed a button.

I won't make any excuse,' said his own voice, *but the pain is insufferable …*

He put back the receiver, then picked it up and dialed the downstairs phone. It was inconceivable that anyone should be at the other end. After the first three or four rings, a click as it switched to the answer phone.

His own voice: *I'm sorry I can't take your message at the moment, but if you'd like to…*

And then what was impossible and in a voice that he'd never heard before: *Every device in this house, when considered according to the long established by-laws of the District, is the property of Ferryman & Co. It has come to our attention that you were unwilling to accept this week's consignment. Expect it to arrive by the weekend. What is to be delivered will be delivered.*

He found a pair of black mittens in a drawer and put them on. Never had the house been so glacial. From the sash window, the sky had an ice-cube, grey-white sheen. His feet on the staircase were strangely silent, as if the wood was too cold to creak. As he edged downwards, his breath unfolded in smoky bouquets. It was almost half an hour before he reached the sitting room. He put an old newspaper and the last of the kindling in the grate. The matches were in the pocket of his inner overcoat; at the third attempt he lit the fire.

It was half past three before he remembered he hadn't eaten all day. He went to the fridge; nothing there or in even a cupboard where he kept the bread and cereals. How could he have gone through his provisions so quickly? Perhaps someone had crept in whilst he was upstairs. A second search was unsuccessful. He'd been certain he had a can of beans a little past its sell by date. But where? He must have thrown it out. There was no choice. He'd have to go outside.

With difficulty, he managed to squeeze some leather gloves over his mittens. He adjusted his scarves and opened the front door. Outside, winter had transfixed a wash of grey-black cloud to a flaking, slate sky. The street and pavement slabs had been wind-scrubbed to a tinny gleam. Only a single brown leaf, abraded with pale gold, reminded him that he had once lived with trees, witnessed the change of seasons, the light turning the shadows on wide lawns – all long before he'd become trapped in what seemed like a perpetual November.

The General Store was closed. Was it the weekend? There were corrugated metal shutters over the windows and a dark blue door, which he could not recall seeing previously, was not only shut but padlocked. There was no notice or any hint of an explanation. He had never known the General Store to shut. Now that he'd thought the matter through, he was certain it was always open at weekends. No doubt there was an explanation. Illness or a death in the family? But where else in the District could he find something to eat? The Bag of Nails? They must serve some food. A ploughman's lunch - or crisps at the very least.

A van, with the familiar Ferryman's logo on the side, drew up beside him. The delivery man, who was in the driver's seat, wound down the window.

As the man leant forward to speak, Plant caught a glimpse of his companion in the passenger seat: an enormous, shaven block of a head. The nose had been replaced by what looked like an axe blade; the pale, not quite human, eyes studying Plant might have been borrowed from a species that could spot its prey from a distance of a mile or more.

"Ah," said the driver. "You're out. Probably just as well because we'll soon be going in. Inside your house. I wouldn't hurry back. My friend here likes to have a look around when he makes a home delivery. See if there's anything that needs … altering."

Even after the van was driven away, Plant remained quite still, as if he'd encountered a creature capable of immobilizing its quarry. It started to rain, thick lines of freezing iron. Already his outer overcoat was heavy. He must make a move.

The lights of The Bag of Nails were on, ambiguously welcoming, as though ready to offer only a sticky, yellow solace, a taste of egg yolk and various poisons. A bell rang as he opened the door. Immediately the strong scent of bygone tobacco and something almost sulphurous. The barman was drawing a pint of deep gold, brown beer; it frothed in the sleeve before settling. He set it on the counter, where it gleamed and effervesced, and then glanced at Plant.

"What are you having? A drink or a story?" said the barman. He switched on an overhead lamp; the black bar gleamed with points of light, as if whole galaxies had just been made visible. After a moment, Plant understood that hundreds and hundreds of nails had been driven into the wood.

"Neither. I'd like something to eat. Do you have a menu?"

Without moving his body apart from his head, the man at the bar turned towards Plant. His mouth was huge, crocodilian; the eyes, heavily lidded; the skin rough and patched with red sores and nests of burst capillaries. "Food is only served with drink in this house," he said. "What are you are having?" He spoke in a deep, upper class boom that seemed inauthentic, not so much the product of upbringing as training; the voice of a would-be theatrical knight.

"That's very civil of you, I'm sure. But I don't take alcohol."

"Good god!" roared the man. "A chap in the Bag of Nails, and he doesn't bloody well drink. Well, that's a first, isn't it, landlord?"

"Mr. Ferryman's right, sir," said the barman, not meeting Plant's eye "The license is very specific on the matter. Food is only to be served with alcohol."

Plant ran his eye along the shelves. Beneath the optics there was a row of miniatures.

"Well in that case, I'll have one of those little bottles of whisky. To take out."

"That's the spirit!"

The barman leant forward. He seemed to be staring at what remained of Plant's mouth.

"I'm sorry, sir," he said. "If you could repeat that."

"The fellow's deaf," bellowed Mr. Ferryman. "Shame really. He's missed out on some bloody fine stories."

Then Plant saw Mr. Ferryman's left hand, the fingers splayed and rigid, the palm flat against the counter, and nailed to it. Nearby were black rivulets of blood that had dried who knows how long ago.

"Useful in its way," said Mr. Ferryman, following his gaze "And a bloody sight easier than rowing. Anyway a gentleman should never fall down just because he's been drinking!"

The barman placed the miniature and a tumbler opposite Mr. Plant. "To drink in, sir. If you'd be so good."

"Now, may I see the menu?" He moved what was left of his mouth slowly. His voice was low and weak, coming from deep within him.

The barman pointed to a glass jar. An elliptical yellow moon swam in viscous brown liquid. A pickled egg?

"Have you got anything else?"

The barman nodded and moved away, no doubt to fetch something from the back.

"I can tell you a story or two about pickled eggs. But perhaps I'd best say a little bit about the pickling process first."

Without warning, Mr. Plant's left hand was being held down firmly. He turned round in time to see the first strike of the hammer, the blood jetting, the nail half driven through the flesh. Then the barman gave it one more tremendous blow and a couple of neat taps, a final touch of artistry. Mr. Plant attempted to cry out; his skin convulsed and thickened, as if to defend veins and arteries beneath its surface. His long howl of pain died away, locked inside him.

"Good lord," said Mr. Ferryman, surprise overcoming his anger at the interruption, "Your mouth has completely sealed over!" His eyes were bright with anticipation and excitement. How many millions of years was it since he'd last had such a ready audience, a companion captive to the finest touch of his every tale?

Lacan on Lynch: Viewing *Twin Peaks* through a Psychoanalytic Lens

By Rob F. Martin

I SOMETIMES FIND it hard to resist channeling Agent Dale Cooper when enjoying a well-brewed cup of "damn good coffee!" So I was quite excited when Showtime announced that it would be working with David Lynch and Mark Frost on a third season of *Twin Peaks*. And this excitement became elation when I learned Lynch would be directing all eighteen episodes.

It was everything I expected. Which means it was nothing like I expected.

After nearly seventeen hours, the main narrative resolves, only to begin a new sequence of circumstances. Then, in the series' final hour, we watch the erasure of all prior events and are left without resolution. We are simply greeted with a closing shot of Cooper sitting in the Red Room, a stunned look of disbelief rolling across his face as Laura Palmer whispers in his ear. It's unsettling, heartbreaking, and existentially beautiful.

As the credits rolled, I sat in stunned silence, trying to make sense of what I'd just seen and how I was feeling. I describe it as a sense of pleasant disappointment—a paradoxical emotion only David Lynch could evoke. That closing shot haunted me through the following week, and as I continued to put the pieces together, I couldn't help but see *Twin Peaks* though the lens of psychoanalyst, Jacques Lacan. According to Lacan, three interwoven threads form the fabric of the human psyche: the Real, the Symbolic, and the Imaginary (the three registers of human reality).

What follows is a synopsis of Lacan's framework. Once this framework has been summarized, we will use it to analyze the metanarrative of the *Twin Peaks* universe, with special emphasis on the aforementioned closing shot.

THE REAL

At its most basic level, the Real can be understood as material reality, the backdrop of life we all share—the way things *actually* are, despite how we may individually *perceive* them. But at a more unconscious level, the Real refers to the trauma arising when some aspect of the material world calls our individual perceptions into question. It is a disruption of our subjective "reality" that shakes our stability, and because the shock it inflicts upon the unconscious is far too great for our fragile minds to endure, the experience cannot be translated into words.

An example of this trauma can be observed in the experience of a deeply religious person as he suffers the breakdown of his worldview. While he desperately wants to hold on to the long cherished beliefs that gave his life meaning and purpose, providing him with a narrative to make sense of existence, he also realizes that he can no longer do so with any intellectual honesty. The foundations of his subjective world crumble against the objective and evidential weight of the external world, and he finds himself in bottomless free fall.

Or think of the child who has learned to trust and find safety in a parental or authority figure, only to have her perceptions of this person shattered through physical and sexual abuse. Now violated, the child has a sense of uncleanness, and she begins sinking in a cesspool of guilt and shame, trying to catch a breath of fresh air above the surface—after all, it must be her fault; Daddy's a good man. The mind would rather have a comforting fable than face the frightening truth.

While these are not the experiences of every person, there is one trauma, according to Lacan, that we all have in common—the universal sense of loss that has been haunting each of us since infancy.

In the early stages of his theory, Lacan suggested that the initial experience of every person was a state of oceanic wholeness, in which we felt no sense of separation from our mothers and the world into which we had been born. In this state, nothing existed beyond our needs, and because our needs were met—what our tiny psyches perceived as a result of our union with everything surrounding us—there was no feeling of lack.

However, somewhere between six and eighteen months of age, we began to realize that we were individuals, alone and isolated behind our eyes, detached from the world to which we once felt connected (this was the birth of our self-consciousness). Gradually, existence became identified with separation, our sense of oneness dissolving into a sense of lack. From then on, we have been unconsciously longing for the wholeness we believe we have lost. We are beings striving to fill our lack, yearning to feel complete once again.

Thus, the Real is the unconscious scar left from the trauma of recognizing our individuality—the shock of losing the initial sense of wholeness we experienced as infants first coming into the world. Our traumas are consistently altering our perceptions, and because they cannot be translated into words, they must be filtered through the Symbolic register.

THE SYMBOLIC

Tad Delay writes, "The Symbolic is everything collected into our psyche from our experiences. It is from our parents and friendships, our social norms and taboos, our gods and our demons. The Symbolic is an intermediate register of sorts, the filter through which the Real enters and becomes interpreted for the Imaginary.... The Symbolic is a stitchwork of trauma, ideals, and experiences that we continually absorb into our unconscious." And these traumas, ideals, and experiences coalesce to form what Lacan called "The Big Other."

The Big Other is the unseen and often stern gaze we feel bearing down on our shoulders, that elusive whisper in our unconscious ear that directs our actions, speech, and thoughts. And because it is a projection of our ideals—which are formed by our traumas and experiences—obedience to the Big Other, we believe, will guide us back to our lost sense of oceanic wholeness.

Thus, the traumatic Real—which cannot be translated into words—is interpreted through the Symbolic to become the Big Other. And the Big Other, through its whisper, unveils the Imaginary—an idealized image of how things ought to be.

THE IMAGINARY

The Imaginary is the unconscious picture of our ideal reality, a realm we dream up and then live within. It is a place where our lack will dissipate, our scars will fade, and wholeness will be attained. But before this can be realized, we must become the ideal image of ourselves—which is possible only through obedience to the Big Other. However, like a cruel taskmaster, the Big Other is never satisfied; we soon find that the more we strive to obey its demands, the more frustrated we become, and the deeper our lack grows. And as we fail to become our ideal self, our ideal reality is called into question. Again, we are faced with a disruption that compounds our trauma—which must then be filtered back through the Symbolic and restructured into a new Imaginary in an unending spiral of frustration.

WE ARE LIKE THE DREAMER WHO DREAMS

In episode 14 of *Twin Peaks: The Return*, FBI Director Gordon Cole speaks with Agents Tammy Preston and Albert Rosenfield. He tells them that he had another "Monica Bellucci dream," in which she called him to set up a meeting at a certain café in Paris. I would suggest that this scene is the interpretive lens through which the entire series be viewed—especially when considering the Lacanian registers.

As Gordon begins explaining the dream, he mentions that Cooper was there when Monica arrived, but that he couldn't see his face—a statement that gets less cryptic as the scene progresses. Gordon sits down with Monica and her friends, and they apparently have a nice time together. Then, at some point in the discussion, she looks to Gordon and says: "We are like the dreamer who dreams, and then lives inside the dream."

Gordon tells her he understands.

She then asks, "But who is the dreamer?"

Gordon is shaken by the question, and Monica begins gazing past him, indicating to him to look back. As he turns, Gordon sees a much younger version of himself (in a scene from *Twin Peaks: Fire Walk With Me*). He sits at his desk in the old Philadelphia office. Cooper crouches before him and explains that he is worried about that particular day—February 16, 1988—because of a dream he had two years prior. However, the discussion is interrupted as Agent Phillips Jeffries storms into the room, points at Cooper, and asks, "Who do you think that is there?"

"Damn!" Gordon says looking back to Tammy and Albert. "I hadn't remembered that. Now this is really something interesting to think about."

Agent Rosenfield, who was also present in the Philadelphia office to witness the incident, agrees. "Yes. I'm beginning to remember that too."

This scene raises questions that, when answered, simply lead to another layer of questions. So, for our purposes here, I am going to leave all but one aside.

BUT WHO IS THE DREAMER?

Monica's line about the dreamer is a phrase out of the *Eternal Stories from the Upanishads*, a collection of small parables based upon the ancient Vedic texts. In context it reads: "We are like the spider. We weave our life, and then move along in it. We are like the dreamer who dreams, and then lives in the dream. This is true for the entire universe. That is why it is said, 'Having created the creation, the Creator entered into it. This is true for us. We create our world, and then enter into that world. We live in the world that we have created. When our hearts are pure, then we create the beautiful, enlightened life we have wished for."

The Upanishads aim to help one realize Brahman—the wholeness of all things; all is one. Brahman is the pure consciousness of the Universe atomized into the individual consciousness of every living creature. We are the Universe witnessing itself, one consciousness experiencing itself subjectively. It is through the realization of Brahman that oceanic wholeness can be regained, where lack is dissolved into bliss, where there is no longer a sense of separation. It is as if the drop of water—the individual Self—has fallen back into the ocean and merged with it.

However, the parable in *Eternal Stories* begs a certain question, which Monica asks: "But who is the dreamer?" From the scene, it seems to me that Cooper, or at least the fundamental *essence* of Cooper, is the dreamer. This is supported when the entirety of the series is considered. In the *Twin Peaks* chronology (if such a thing even exists at this point), a little over a year after the incident with Jeffries, Cooper has another dream, as seen in Episode 2 of Season One. This is significant when we remember the series' closing shot—Laura whispering into Cooper's ear as his eyes dissolve into empty pools of hopelessness—and view it through a Lacanian lens.

COOPER IN THE RED ROOM

Although the series ends with Cooper back in the Red Room, I cannot help but speculate: perhaps he has always been there; perhaps he has never left. Consider the structure of *Fire Walk With Me*. The film is a prequel chronicling the days leading up to Laura's murder, but as we watch these events unfold, we notice that Cooper seems to already be in the Red Room and psychically connected to her.

So, in a Lacanian framework, Cooper, or the *essence* that is Cooper, is a self-conscious entity suffering the trauma of realizing its individuality, separated and isolated behind a single pair of eyes. Haunted with lack, he yearns for oceanic wholeness; he longs for Brahman.

Thus, Cooper's traumatic Real is taken into the Symbolic. Though this, he dreams up his idyllic world within the Imaginary— the small town of Twin Peaks, which he at one point describes as a place of dignity and honor, where every life has meaning; "it's a way of life I thought had vanished from the earth." He then steps into this world as the idealized image of himself—a respected FBI agent called in to solve the murder of the town sweetheart.

However, rather than merely *solving* the murder, he *undoes* it. And in undoing the murder, he undoes his idealized self, because the realization of his idealized self was contingent on the events generated by the murder. We then view the unraveling of Cooper in the person of Richard (a sort of hybrid of Cooper and his evil Doppelganger) as he searches for Laura. Only when he finds her, she is no longer Laura, but Carrie Page—a waitress who needs to leave town after killing a man in her living room.

Cooper's unraveling reaches its completion as he and Carrie stand in the street in front of Laura's childhood home—which is no longer owned by the Palmers; in fact, in this new reality, they have never lived there. He wonders aloud what year it is, and Carrie becomes visibly troubled. She begins to hear Sarah Palmer calling Laura's name the morning after her murder, and with an ear-shattering scream, she looks up at the house as the lights go out and the closing shot slowly fades in.

This closing shot is similar to something we see twenty-five years earlier, in the aforementioned scene in Episode 2 of Season One. While sleeping in the Great Northern Hotel, Cooper has a dream. In it, he sees himself sitting in the Red Room; only he is twenty-five years older. Across from him is a woman resembling Laura Palmer. She stands, walks over to him, kisses him, and then whispers into his ear (we learn later that she whispered the killer's name). Perhaps, Cooper's "dream" is merely his waking up in the Red Room, and the actual dream—his Imaginary—is his experience as an FBI agent in Twin Peaks.

LAURA IS THE ONE

If the "Cooper essence" is the dreamer, then what is Laura's role in all of this? Episode 10 of *The Return* gives us some clues, in a scene in which Deputy Hawk receives a call from the Log Lady.

"Hawk, the electricity is humming," she says with weak, dying breaths. "You hear it in the mountains and rivers, you see it dance among the seas and stars, and glowing around the moon, but in these days, the glow is dying. What will be in the darkness that remains? The Truman brothers are both true men. They are your brothers. And the others, the good ones, who have been with you. Now the circle is almost complete. Watch and listen to the dream of time and space. It all comes out now, flowing like a river. That which is, and is not. Hawk, Laura is the one."

In the *Twin Peaks* universe, electricity serves as the means through which an individual Self transmigrates through parallel realities (where the Cooper essence bounces between Dale the FBI agent, Richard, and Dougie Jones). But the glow—the good and true—is dying, and darkness is crouching at the threshold, ready consume all there is. However, the Log Lady tells Hawk to listen to the dream of time and space as it comes flowing out like a river. Everything that is and has been and will be flows from this river of dreams. And Laura is the one from which this river springs.

That is, Laura is Cooper's Big Other, whispering the dream into his ear, closing the circle—which is merely an infinite loop of frustration that, through the Symbolic, alters itself into a different Imaginary with each new underlying trauma.

And so, *Twin Peaks* leaves us with that final shot—of a self-conscious entity suffering the trauma of realizing its individuality, longing for oceanic wholeness, and tormented by the implacable demands of the Big Other.

soul of a mannequin

By Justyna Bendyk

In a dusty, crowded attic butterflies were singing
their colors created an iris and shade of skin
for a broken doll
with a hole instead of a heart
and red paint stains
instead of tears

what I saw were tutu skirts the color of angels' wings
fragile egos in fragile mirrors
children's voices begging
only for fun
bending their knees only before the sun

the silence was blending with its mind painfully
stiffness was becoming its body
and it wanted to be just a toy once again
but only in innocent hands
an object of passion and love and kisses

let me be your fragile angel who does not speak
does not judge
angel, demon, clown
clean those sad smudges on your cheeks with my own skin
admire me as clouds' shapes on a sky

because nobody looked at him
it died
In a dusty, crowded attic butterflies were singing
burying a toy child thirsty for love

Shirley Jackson and That Old Black Magic

By Jill Hand

A WITCH caught me when I was twelve.

She caught me the usual way witches catch their child victims: by enticement. In my case the bait wasn't a house made out of candy, like the one in Hansel and Gretel. It was a book called *Life Among the Savages*. I bought it at a Scholastic Book Fair and liked it so much I went back the next day and bought the sequel, *Raising Demons*.

Remember Scholastic Book Fairs? The pungent smell of new paperbacks that hit you as soon as you walked in? To a book lover, that new-ink-and-paper smell equals pure happiness. If you were a kid who liked to read, there were few finer things in life than a Scholastic Book Fair.

So, there was twelve-year-old me, a voracious reader (I'd already ruined my eyes by reading under the covers at night with a flashlight) with money in my pocket and an array of books to choose from. By then I'd read nearly everything in the school library, including an odd volume dating from the reign of Queen Victoria called *The Water Babies.*[1] It was written by an Anglican priest in support of Darwin's theory of evolution and contained a surprising amount of prejudice against the Irish. What it was doing in a school library in New Jersey was anybody's guess.

Life Among the Savages and *Raising Demons* were miles better than *The Water Babies.* I read them over and over, delighting in Jackson's deadpan humor as she described life with four rambunctious children in two big old houses in Vermont. Her tone was similar to that of an anthropologist studying the activities of a primitive tribe whose members are neither cooperative nor appreciative of being studied. They're very funny books.

I can still recite entire passages from those two books, fifty years later. That's how much Shirley Jackson has gotten under my skin. There are echoes of her in Stephen King's writing and that of Neil Gaiman and Donna Tartt, all of whom have professed admiration for her work. I like to think there are traces of her in my own weird fiction.

As a mother with four young children, meal preparation was a preoccupation of Jackson's. Food figures prominently in her work, most strikingly in *We Have Always Lived in the Castle,* where she has the precocious, feral Merricat say, "We eat the year away. We eat the spring and the summer and the fall. We wait for something to grow and then we eat it."[2]

---

[1] Charles Kingsley, *The Water Babies: A Fairy Tale for a Lana-Baby* (London: Macmillan and Co., 1863).

[2] Shirley Jackson, *We Have Always Lived in the Castle* (New York: Viking Press, 1962), 45.

Food imagery crops up in her lecture, "Notes for a Young Writer," where she advises fledgling writers to throw in a little "garlic" occasionally when writing fiction. That's how she described a "wholly inappropriate word, or startling phrase" to draw the reader up short, or in her words "make him stop dead and think." An example she gave was "pretty as a skunk."[3]

Agatha Christie, one of Jackson's favorite authors, made use of the same technique, calling the bait she used to keep her readers engaged "plums."

Jackson was an admirer of Christie and a great reader of crime fiction. In one of her lectures, she expressed disappointment that real life wasn't more like a mystery novel. She claimed to have once asked her local pharmacist where she could get enough arsenic to poison a family of six, only to be told that the drugstore didn't carry any. She thought his counterpart in a Christie story would have called the police.

In many ways Jackson's humor is reminiscent of James Thurber and Dorothy Parker, both of whom wrote for *The New Yorker* at one time or another. However, Jackson's humor, while mordent at times, was less caustic than Parker's, who could be a terror as a critic, famously once saying that a performance by Katherine Hepburn "ran the gamut of emotions from A to B." She was kinder to Jackson, having high praise for her work. In her last review for *Esquire,* Parker wrote of *We Have Always Lived in the Castle,* "This novel brings back all my faith in terror and death. I can say no higher of it and her."[4]

---

[3] Shirley Jackson, *Come Along with Me: Part of a Novel, Sixteen Stories and Three Lectures,* edited by Stanley Edgar Hyman (New York: Viking Press, 1968), 251.

[4] Dorothy Parker, "Shudders: Quiet and Cumulative," *Esquire,* December 1962, 44.

Jackson, when not scaring the daylights out of people, was like Thurber in that she was a master of casting a loving eye on the ridiculous.

Compare Thurber's "The Night the Ghost Got In" to Jackson's "The Night We All Had Grippe,"[5] and you'll find the same bemused, reportorial style of describing a mysterious domestic event. Then there's Phoebe, the loopy housekeeper in *Life Among the Savages* who presents Jackson's husband with a plate of cookies iced with the words SINNER, REPENT. Phoebe is reminiscent of Gertie, one of the Thurbers' maids. Gertie comes home drunk one morning and stumbles around, bumping into furniture, causing Thurber's mother to call downstairs and ask what on earth she was doing. "Dusting," she replies.[6]

That same wry style of middle-class suburban humor was employed by syndicated columnist Erma Bombeck and by Jean Kerr, author of "Please Don't Eat the Daisies," a 1957 collection of essays that became the basis for a film starring Doris Day and a TV series. It was witchcraft that set Jackson apart from Bombeck and Kerr and from other proto-mommy bloggers.

Shortly after the publication of her collection of short stories, *The Lottery: or, The Adventures of James Harris,* in March of 1949, it was reported that Jackson was a practicing witch who owned hundreds of grimoires and books about the supernatural. She even named her half-dozen black cats after lords of Hell. (Most of them were virtually identical, a deliberate ploy to fool her husband, literary critic Stanley Edgar Hyman, into failing to realize they owned so many cats, or so the story goes.)

A story spread by publicist Pyke Johnson claimed Jackson fashioned a wax voodoo doll of publisher Alfred Knopf and made

---

[5] Shirley Jackson, *Let Me Tell You: New Stories, Essays, and Other Writings,* edited by Laurence Jackson Hyman and Sarah Hyman DeWitt (New York: Random House, 2015), 133.

[6] James Thurber, "A Sequence of Servants," *My Life and Hard Times* (New York: Harper & Brothers, 1933), 46.

him break a leg while he was skiing in Vermont. It was allegedly done in retaliation for Knopf's refusal to give Hyman an increase in his advance for a book he was writing. Jackson quipped that she had to wait until Knopf crossed the border from New York into Vermont before she could put a hex on him because she was forbidden by law from practicing witchcraft over state lines.[7]

The witchcraft angle caught on, famously spurred by a profile W.G. Rogers wrote for the Associated Press in which he said Jackson wrote "not with a pen but with a broomstick."[8]

That phrase was frequently quoted, although if you think about it, it would be impractical if not impossible, but it made for good copy.

"She says she can break a man's leg and throw a girl down an elevator shaft. Such things happen she says!" Rogers wrote breathlessly.[9]

Jackson's side of the story was that she'd had a couple of drinks and thought it would be fun to claim to be a witch. It worked, as she'd shrewdly guessed it would. In many ways the post-World War II era, with its emphasis on conformity and its atmosphere of near-hysterical paranoia, was similar to that of Puritan New England during the Salem witch trials. Jackson wouldn't have failed to recognize this. Her historical fiction for children, *The Witchcraft of Salem Village,* has a young girl express delight in having a new cloak to wear to a witch-hanging. Like "The Lottery," it is chilling in its brisk, businesslike description of a community turning on its own.[10]

Along with the fear of Communism and the atomic bomb, belief in the occult was making a comeback in the years immediately following World War II. It would really get rolling a decade later,

---

[7] Ruth Franklin, *Shirley Jackson: A Rather Haunted Life* (New York: Liveright Publishing Corp., 2017), 108.

[8] W.G. Rogers, "Literary Guidepost," *Associated Press,* April 13, 1949.

[9] Ibid.

[10] Shirley Jackson, *The Witchcraft of Salem Village,* New York: Random House, 1956.

with the television show *Bewitched* and *Rosemary's Baby* and Anton LaVey's campy Church of Satan. But the seeds had been planted. John Van Drutten's 1950 play, *Bell, Book and Candle,* about a modern young witch went on to become a movie starring Kim Novak and James Stewart. In 1956, a book about a Colorado housewife who professed to recall a past life as a 19th century Irishwoman named Bridey Murphy became a best seller.[11]

Jackson was thirty-one when "The Lottery" appeared in the June 26, 1948 issue of *The New Yorker.* She had been writing and publishing short stories for nearly a decade, starting in 1941 with a lighthearted description of her experiences working in retail called "My Life with R.H. Macy."[12] But this story was different. It caused an immediate sensation. Letters poured in to the magazine. Some were from people who were furious and wanted to cancel their subscription. Others wanted to know where they could go to watch the ritual being carried out. Everyone was curious about the author.

"I have been assured over and over that if it had been the only story I ever wrote or published, there would be people who would not forget my name. Of the three-hundred-odd letters that I received that summer I can count only thirteen that spoke kindly to me, and they were mostly from friends. Even my mother scolded me," she said in a 1960 lecture.[13]

Who was the woman who'd written about a small town where residents draw lots to stone someone to death? She needed an angle, one that explained how a nice lady who wrote bright pieces about her children for mass market publications like *Woman's Day and Good Housekeeping* could have written "The Lottery" or "The

---

[11] Morey Bernstein, *The Search for Bridey Murphy,* New York: Doubleday & Co., 1956.

[12] Shirley Jackson, "My Life with R.H. Macy," *The New Republic,* Dec. 22, 1941.

[13] Shirley Jackson, *Come Along with Me: Part of a Novel, Sixteen Stories and Three Lectures,* edited by Stanley Edgar Hyman (New York: Viking Press, 1968), 223.

Daemon Lover," in which a woman's happiness on her wedding day turns to anxiety and then to panic as she waits for a bridegroom who never arrives.

Who is Jamie Harris, the fair-haired young man who romances an older woman only to vanish with no explanation? He may be a cruel prankster or he may not exist, except in the nameless woman's imagination. Then again, he may be a demon who goes by the name James Harris or James Herries, from the old Scottish and English ballads anthologized by Francis James Child. Jackson was fond of the traditional folk ballads, with their themes of wronged lovers and gruesome murders.[14]

The sense of doubt after finishing "The Daemon Lover" is frustrating. If readers hoped for closure, for Jamie to appear with a dozen roses and an apology, they were disappointed. But then again, a story like that would be forgettable. Its ending which is no ending at all is what makes it memorable.

Jackson followed M.R. James' dictum that in order to work, chilling tales should seem as though they could happen in real life. "Let us, then, be introduced to the actors in a placid way; let us see them going about their ordinary business, undisturbed by forebodings, pleased with their surroundings; and into this calm environment let the ominous thing put out its head, unobtrusively at first, and then more insistently, until it holds the stage," James wrote.[15]

Like James, Jackson specialized in the slow, calmly paced buildup to a jarring crescendo. Sometimes the crescendo is strongly hinted at but never described. Such is the case with "The Lottery." We never see the stones being hurled at Tessie, although we're not left with any hope that rescue will arrive. The same holds true with

---

[14] Francis James Child, *The English and Scottish Popular Ballads,* Boston: Houghton, Mifflin & Co., 1904.

[15] M.R. James, *A Warning to the Curious and Other Ghost Stories* (London: Edward Arnold & Co., 1925), vi.

"The Summer People," in which all is well with a couple who own a summer cottage until the year they decide to stay on after Labor Day. The locals express shock. A series of inconveniences follows. The kerosene delivery is inadequate, the grocery store stops making deliveries, and the locals seem *really* concerned by the couple's insistence on staying longer than usual. Nothing bad happens by the end of the story, but there's a nearly unbearable feeling of tension that something surely will.[16]

Witchcraft served Jackson as a half-joking explanation for why a young mother was able to write such frightening stories. Witches, after all, are thought to be familiar with darkness. It explained why she was equally adept at writing cozily about her own houses, filled with children and pets, with closets so full of jackets and boots and sports equipment that their doors wouldn't close, toys everywhere, including "the little wheels off things" as she was writing about the definitely un-cozy Hill House.[17]

The Haunting of Hill House is Jackson's classic 1959 Gothic novel. The premise of a paranormal investigator placing a classified ad in a newspaper asking for volunteers to study a haunted house was probably inspired by a famous paranormal investigation carried out by ghost hunter Harry Price. He ran an ad in the May 25, 1937 edition of *The Times* of London seeking "responsible persons of leisure and intelligence, intrepid, critical, and unbiased" to assist in his investigation of Borley Rectory. Ever the showman, Price called the red-brick Victorian monstrosity in rural Essex, "the most haunted house in England."[18]

Jackson has two female volunteers, Eleanor and Theodora, answer the ad placed by her supernatural investigator, Dr. John Montague. In Price's case, all of his forty-eight volunteer observers

---

[16] Shirley Jackson, "The Summer People," *Charm,* September, 1950, 268-269.

[17] Shirley Jackson, *Life Among the Savages* (New York: Farrar, Straus, 1953), 2.

[18] Harry Price, *The Most Haunted House in England: Ten Years' Investigation of Borley Rectory* (London: Longmans, Green & Co., 1940), 106.

were male, keen young Englishmen who spent freezing nights on a cot in the rectory's library, waiting in vain for a glimpse of the spectral nun or the phantom coach and horses said to haunt the grounds.

Eleanor and Theodora were deliberately chosen due to their having had personal experiences with the paranormal. In that way, Jackson anticipated the swarms of ghost hunters on reality TV shows in the early 2000s, all of whom claimed to have seen a ghost at one time or another.

Jackson's stories about her children helped keep the family afloat financially while Hyman labored for years over *The Armed Vision,* his book on literary criticism methodology. During a time when a married woman couldn't get a credit card without her husband's approval, Jackson sold her work to magazines, squeezing time at her Royal typewriter in between ferrying the children to and from school, household chores, and the babies' naps.

She describes her dual identity in "The Third Baby's the Easiest," from *Life Among the Savages.* In October of 1948, four months after "The Lottery" appeared in *The New Yorker,* she goes to the hospital to deliver Sarah, the third of her four children. The nurse checking her in asks for her profession. "Writer," Jackson says, to which the nurse replies, "Housewife."

"Writer," Jackson says again.

"I'll just put down housewife," the nurse tells her.[19]

We can picture Jackson gritting her teeth.

No wonder she preferred being identified as "a practicing amateur witch," writing in a biographical blurb to her publisher that she drew protective charms in black crayon on the door sills and window ledges of her homes to keep out demons.[20]

---

[19] Shirley Jackson, *Life Among the Savages* (New York: Farrar, Straus, 1953), 66.

[20] Shirley Jackson, *Let Me Tell You: New Stories, Essays, and Other Writing* (New York: Random House, 2015), 357.

Being a witch beat being a housewife. Witches had power, and life was no picnic for an overweight woman with frizzy red hair whose notoriously unfaithful husband was surrounded all day by pretty, young girls. Bennington, where Hyman taught, was an all-female college at the time. Jackson was displeased with her role of faculty wife, which relegated her to the background at parties where students eagerly flocked around her husband, hanging on his every word.

After Jackson's death at forty-eight from heart failure in the summer of 1965, Hyman went on to marry one of his former students.

In "On Being a Faculty Wife," first published in *Mademoiselle,* one of the students asks Jackson where she and Hyman met. She replies that they met in college.

"You went to college? How many years?"

"Four."

"Gosh. How come you ended up doing housework and stuff? Couldn't you get a job?"[21]

Jackson struggled with agoraphobia. It had been slowly creeping up on her for years but it became full-blown after the publication of *We Have Always Lived in the Castle*.[22]

Going out in public, even to the North Bennington post office or the grocery store grew to be terrifying. Today she would probably be diagnosed with social anxiety, a problem recognizable to those who find monsters sometimes wear the faces of their neighbors. That's why "The Lottery" still packs a punch after all these years. The fear we feel in reading it stems from our knowledge of the evil seemingly ordinary people are capable of. As Sartre famously put it, "Hell is other people."

---

[21] Shirley Jackson, "On Being a Faculty Wife," *Mademoiselle,* December 1956, 116-117.

[22] Ruth Franklin, *Shirley Jackson: A Rather Haunted Life* (New York: Liveright Publishing Corp., 2017), 4.

Jackson gave us monsters whose faces we might see at PTA meetings and across the dinner table. She's like Nathaniel Hawthorne in that respect. He was keenly aware of the kind of wickedness cloaked in respectability of which his New England brethren were capable.

While Jackson's childhood was spent in a wealthy suburb of San Francisco, New England is where she lived for most of her life. Her writing reflects a sparse, carefully pruned Gothic sensibility that's pure New England in its matter-of-fact approach to ghosts and bloodshed and dealings with the Devil.

Take the villagers in her short story "The Renegade," who suggest to Mrs. Walpole, a transplant from the city, various cruel ways to prevent her dog Lady from chasing and killing chickens.[23] They're exactly like people we might meet today in rural Maine or Vermont: gossipy and full of unsolicited advice. Mrs. Walpole's children, who pet Lady while telling her she should be fitted with a spiked collar that will cut off her head, are cheerfully ghoulish, like children we might know. They're savages, as Jackson lovingly referred to her own children in her first collection of memoirs.

It's been said that Jackson was a one-trick pony, her claim to fame stemming primarily from having written "The Lottery." That's incorrect. She wrote six novels and two hundred short stories. In addition to *The Haunting of Hill House,* she wrote *The Road Through the Wall,* about murder and suicide, and *Hangsman,* about a college student who has a nervous breakdown, and *The Bird's Nest,* about a woman with multiple personalities. She wrote *We Have Always Lived in the Castle,* in which one of the characters has poisoned nearly every one of her relatives. She wrote *The Sundial,* in which an eccentric family and their hangers-on gather to await the end of the world.

The Sundial is a thoroughly funny book, cheerfully relating how wealthy Lionel Halloran was pushed down the stairs of his mansion

---

[23] Shirley Jackson, "The Renegade," *Harper's,* November 1949, 234.

and killed by his own mother. At one point, tired of looking after her murderous mother-in-law, Lionel's widow turns to her young daughter, Fancy.

"Maybe she will drop dead on the doorstep. Fancy dear, would you like to see Granny drop dead on the doorstep?"

"Yes, mother," the child replies.[24]

Children frequently have the funniest lines in Jackson's stories. In "Charles," her son Laurie gleefully recounts the misdeeds of a naughty kindergarten boy to the mingled horror and fascination of Jackson and her husband.[25] (Charles and Laurie turn out to be one and the same, as Jackson learns when she goes to the first PTA meeting of the year, hoping to meet Charles' unfortunate mother.)

While she loved her children, Jackson preferred not to be thought of as a housewife, as she told the nurse. Like Midge Maisel, the 1950s housewife turned standup comic in the Amazon TV series *The Marvelous Mrs. Maisel,* she had other talents. Unlike the slender Midge, who keeps a little book in which she daily records her measurements to make sure she hasn't gained weight since college, Jackson was notoriously careless of her physical appearance. It was her work that mattered, a philosophy at odds with today's Snapchat mommies who carefully curate every aspect of their lives that they present to the outside world in an effort to make themselves and their families appear enviably flawless.

What would Jackson think of Snapchat? Probably not much. She knew it was the flaws, or the "garlic," that make life interesting.

---

[24] Shirley Jackson, *The Sundial* (New York: Farrar, Straus, 1958), 1.
[25] Shirley Jackson, *Life Among the Savages* (New York: Farrar, Straus, 1953), 22.

Bibliography

Bernstein, Morey. *The Search for Bridey Murphy.* New York: Doubleday & Co., 1956.

Child, Francis James. *The English and Scottish Popular Ballads.* Boston: Houghton, Mifflin & Co., 1904.

Franklin, Ruth. *Shirley Jackson: A Rather Haunted Life.* New York: Liveright Publishing Corp., 2017.

Jackson, Shirley. *Come Along with Me: Part of a Novel, Sixteen Stories and Three Lectures.* edited by Stanley Edgar Hyman. New York: Viking Press, 1968.

— *Let Me Tell You: New Stories, Essays, and Other Writings.* edited by Laurence Jackson Hyman and Sarah Hyman DeWitt. New York: Random House, 2015.

— *Life Among the Savages.* New York: Farrar, Straus, 1953.

— "My Life with R.H. Macy." *Mademoiselle* (December 22, 1941). 862.

— "On Being a Faculty Wife." *The New Republic* (December, 1956). 116-17.

— "The Renegade." *Harper's* (November, 1949). 234.

— "The Summer People." *Charm* (September, 1950). 268-269.

— *The Sundial.* New York: Farrar, Straus. 1958.

— *We Have Always Lived in the Castle.* New York: Viking Press, 1962.

— *The Witchcraft of Salem Village.* New York: Random House, 1956.

James, M.R. *A Warning to the Curious and Other Ghost Stories.* London: Edward Arnold & Co., 1925.

Kingsley, Charles. *The Water Babies: A Fairy Tale for a Land-Baby.* London: Macmillan and Co., 1863.

Parker, Dorothy. "Shudders: Quiet and Cumulative." *Esquire* (December, 1962). 44.

Price, Harry. *The Most Haunted House in England: Ten Years' Investigation of Borley Rectory.* London: Longmans, Green & Co., 1940.

Rogers, W.G. "Literary Guidepost." *Associated Press* (April 13, 1949).

Artist: Øyvind Lauvdahl

How to be a Horror Writer

By Tim Waggoner

IF YOU WANT to be a horror writer, be washed from your mother's womb in a river of blood, kicking and screaming, writhing like an annoyed insect larva released from its egg. Feel rubber glove-covered hands clamp tight on a tiny arm and leg and pull you the rest of the way free. Wail at the loss of the warm, wet dark, which is all you've ever known, scream in terror as harsh light stabs your eyes, shudder as cold air rakes your skin like a thousand claws of ice.

You look upon the face of the giant that holds you, its eyes all that's visible, other features concealed by cloth. There's another faceless giant present, and together they carry you to a small table and place you on a scratchy white cloth beneath a blazing miniature sun. You continue screaming as these horrible, faceless creatures touch and probe you. You fight as best you can, but you're so small compared to them, so weak. They can do anything to you that they want, anything at all, and there's nothing you can do to stop them. They could tear the limbs from your body with ease, place a hand over your nose and mouth, sealing them shut. They could jam a thumb into your fontanel, sink the digit into your small brain and stir shit around in there. And when they finish, when they've had their fun, they could hurl you to the tiled floor to see how many times you bounce, maybe kick you back and forth like some sort of grisly toy. But the Faceless Ones do none of those things. They clean you off, take some measurements, wash you, and then one of the giants wraps you in a thin, soft blanket. You like the cloth. It's tight against your body, and you find this comforting. You grow quiet then, as much from weariness as from relief.

You're carried to a bed where a third giant lies. This one's face is bare, skin wan and coated with a sheen of sweat. You are held out to this new giant, and it reaches ungloved hands to you, lips pulling tight, ends curling upward. You find the expression as hideous as it is alien. The giant takes you and draws you close to its chest. The giant gazes at you with an expression you cannot read. Maybe it's happy to see you, maybe it wants to sink its teeth into your tender flesh. How can you know for certain what dark thoughts swim behind those large eyes?

The giant's lips part and sound emerges from its mouth.

"Hi, little one. I'm your mommy."

You have no idea what the sounds mean, but they feel familiar, or rather, the voice that speaks them does. You think you've heard it before, numerous times, but it was always softer before, muffled. Now it's loud and grating.

It comes to you then, less of a thought than an instinctive realization, something buried deep in your genetic code. This pale, sweaty thing holding you is your home. Only now you're looking at it from the outside. Until this instant, you had no concept of *inside* or *outside*, of being *a part* and being *apart.* This creature from which you emerged is large, yes, but when you were inside, the warm dark was the entire universe, and you were at the center of it. But now you begin to understand that existence is somehow both larger and smaller than the Warm Dark, and that not only aren't you the center of everything, you're so much smaller and weaker than everything around you.

You take a deep breath then, hold it for a moment, and then you let forth an ear-splitting shriek that, if it was a word, would be *No* repeated over and over.

If you want to be a horror writer, go to your Uncle Red's funeral when you're nine. He's not the first dead person you've seen. He's your great-uncle, and you have spent weekends at his house – along with your great-aunt Becky and great-grandmother Alfretta – as long as you can remember. Uncle Red, Aunt Becky, and Great-Grandma have always taken you with them when they do old people stuff, like shopping at flea markets, visiting sick people in the hospital, or attending viewings of recently deceased friends and acquaintances. You have no idea how many viewings you've been to, maybe as many as a dozen, but while you found it awkward to be the only child present, the dead never bothered you. You knew they were dead in an abstract sense, but they all looked more like mannequins than people: skin waxy, eyes sunken, cheeks hollow, too much makeup on their faces.

But as Aunt Becky leads you up to the coffin, clutching your hand, her flesh thin as paper, bones underneath as light and fragile as a bird's, you know that this time is going to be different than those others. You're not afraid, and you don't feel nervous. Your stomach doesn't sink, there's no roaring in your ears, and you're not hit with a sudden wave of dizziness. You feel numb and disconnected, as if only part of you is present and the rest is somewhere else. As the two of you stand next to the coffin, your first thought – which you're too young to realize is a cliché – is that your uncle looks so natural, almost as if he might sit up at any moment, open his eyes, give a huge grin and say, *Gotcha!* Everyone would gasp and then burst into laughter accompanied by tears of joy and relief. But he doesn't move, of course. In fact, his body possesses a profound stillness that disturbs you on a primal level. The living are never so still, not even when sleeping. There's always some movement or sound, however slight. But there's nothing inside your uncle, aside from chemicals designed to slow his body's decay, and it's this Great Nothingness which disturbs you on a level so deep you cannot consciously touch it, let alone name it.

In the monster movies you love to watch on *Shock Theater*, hosted by Dr. Creep, death is embodied by some horrible creature emerging from the darkness, eyes wide with hunger, teeth bared, claws outstretched. In the movies, death is both awful and awesome, in the original sense of those words. It is, in its dark way, majestic and special. A monstrous beast, a servant of ultimate darkness, comes for you – *especially* for you – because you are the *victim*, and without victims, there can be no monsters. But there's nothing special about what's happened to Uncle Red. What's happened to him is no more remarkable than someone flipping a light switch to the off position. An everyday event – common, mundane, and utterly banal.

In the weeks and months to come, you will become obsessed with the idea that Time robs us of our life one moment after another, that it steals whatever happiness we can find even as it gives it to us. This obsession grows worse after you almost drown in a lake while on vacation with your family that summer. You ask your mom and dad what they would've done if you'd died. *We probably wouldn't go on vacation ever again*, they answer. They don't take you to see a psychologist. Only crazy people need a psychologist. It takes a couple years, but eventually you make an uneasy peace with Time. Yes, it takes, but it also gives. It brings new experiences, growth and healing. None of those things would be possible without Time. This realization helps, and you're able to go on with your life, but you never smile as broadly as you did when you were a child, never laugh so easily.

If you want to be a horror writer, learn to live with depression. It's your heritage, after all. Your mother is an agoraphobic who sometimes goes days without speaking, and your father – the very definition of an enabler – does little to help her. Only crazy people go to psychologists, remember? You don't know why she's like this. Your maternal grandmother, who you've always known as Nana, once told you that your mother was married before she met your father and that her first husband abused her, although Nana didn't elaborate on the nature of this abuse, leaving your imagination to fill in the details for you. You wonder if whatever that man did to her made her like this. Years later, you'll decide her depression – like yours – is primarily biochemical, but for now you live with her stillness and silence, and while she's not as still or silent as the dead, she might as well be.

If you want to be a horror writer, internalize your parents' warnings – often unspoken or given obliquely – that the world is a dangerous place, that's it's safest to stay home, but if you do go out, always be careful, always keep watch. Your sister's high school boyfriend is killed when he flips his car over one night after they argue, and when your brother is twenty, he'll have a stroke that changes him forever. Your older relatives begin dying one by one, and you hear stories of kids you knew in school dying in accidents or by their own hands or – once – because they are stationed in Beirut and happened to be sleeping in the barracks when a terrorist drives a truck filled with explosives into the building. You get married and develop testicular cancer when your first daughter is only a few months old, and you're terrified that you'll die before you have a chance to be a father to her. You survive, but you'll always know that your body can betray you at any moment, that it eventually will one way or another, thanks to your old friend Time.

Your mother dies at fifty-nine when your daughter is two, and you won't cry at her funeral. People will think it's because you're being strong, but it's really because you're relieved that she's gone. It's like someone opened a window and let fresh air in. You think it's a profoundly sad thing when someone's death makes the world a better place, but there it is.

You have a second daughter. Nana ends her days in an "assisted living" facility, really an unassisted dying facility as far as you're concerned. It takes years for her to go, and by the end her mind is almost gone, and she'll think your teenage daughter is your wife.

So yeah, the world's a dangerous place. When has it ever been otherwise? But it's the only world you have.

If you want to be a horror writer, divorce your wife. It's not a spectacular break-up. No hurled epithets or objects. Just a slow withering as your wife finds more excuses to avoid spending time with you. You come to understand that she finds your need to be connected to her emotionally burdensome and that she's never truly enjoyed your company. A therapist will ask you to describe your marriage, and you'll say it's like you're a rock on the shore of a cold ocean. The sky is always gray, and wind and rain constantly buffet you. You end up in a shitty one-bedroom apartment that you share with too many roaches. You see your daughters half of the week, and the other half you feel like a ghost haunting your own life. You watch too many true-crime shows on TV because after paying spousal and child support – not to mention the debt payments on the bankruptcy your ex forced you into – you don't have any money to go anywhere or do anything. You only keep the damned cable so the kids have something to watch when they're over. Your ex takes the kids to her mother's for Christmas, and you spend the holiday watching police solve crimes with the latest forensic technology while you eat a festive meal of a single poached egg on a slice of toast.

You don't drink much, and you don't start now. You fear if you start, you won't stop. You find yourself contemplating suicide, not *too* seriously, but the idea seems increasingly appealing. Periodically, you find yourself staring at your reflection in the bathroom mirror – you're not sure why – and you speak these words: *There is no point to your continued existence.* Your reflection doesn't disagree with you. A friend of yours refers to depression as the Black Dog, and you think that's as good a name as any. You start taking meds to hold your own Black Dog at bay, and while they help, the damned thing remains close by, patiently waiting for a chance to bound forward and sink its teeth into your throat.

After a while, you start dating again, not that you have the money for it, but you're sick of being alone, and you're afraid of what you might do if you remain on your own. You try online dating, but the women you're matched with are incompatible at best and downright psychotic at worst. Still, you keep trying.

A blond woman arranges to meet you on Valentine's Day at a bar in a town an hour-and-a-half from your shitty apartment. She has large breasts, and she refers to them constantly during your conversation, as if they're the most important thing about her. She downs one drink after another, and she eventually asks you back to her condo. You didn't date much before you married, and you're surprised by how many women ask you to go home with them or go to your place, after only talking to you for a couple hours. Don't they know that the world is a dangerous place?

She continues drinking once you get to her home, slamming down so much alcohol that you don't see how she remains standing. It's winter, and an ice storm is starting outside, and while you know you should start heading home before the roads get too bad, you can't bring yourself to leave. You're not especially attracted to this woman. She's physically beautiful, but her personality is repellent. But you can't stand the thought of going back to your empty excuse for a life, so you stay, and before long the two of you end up in her bedroom, naked. She displays the breasts she's so proud of, and then smacks her fists into their sides.

"I don't have any sensation in my tits," she says. "You can do anything to them, and I won't feel it. Weird, huh?"

You don't have a condom on you – you'd think by now you'd learn to bring some considering how many women are eager to hop into the sack on the first date – so you take care of her with your mouth and hands. She comes, and you're surprised she feels it, considering how much alcohol is in her system.

"Your turn," she says with a drowsy smile. And then she starts going down on you.

The woman doesn't just suck your dick. She suctions it as if she's an industrial vacuum. The pressure is constant and unrelenting, and you find nothing remotely sexual in the action. There's a kind of mechanical desperation in the woman's efforts, and while you've avoided drinking much tonight – you've got a long drive home, after all – you wish you were drunk now, because what she's doing doesn't feel good. It *hurts.* You wouldn't be surprised if she sucks your dick off and swallows it, like a constrictor devouring its prey.

You are so repelled by what's happening, your dick goes soft, but the woman doesn't stop. If anything, she works more frantically to get you hard again. You're about to ask her to stop when you feel a strange sensation. It's kind of like you're about to orgasm, but how can you if your dick's soft? You do come then, quickly and perfunctorily. When you're finished, the woman raises her head from your crotch and gives you an accusing look.

"What the hell was *that?*" she demands.

"I don't know," you say truthfully.

She says it a couple more times, placing emphasis on a different word each time.

"What the hell *was* that? What the *hell* was that?"

You quickly get dressed and get the hell out of there. It's after two in the morning, and icy rain is coming down heavy, but you don't care. You get in your car – a beat-up Camry that you haven't been able to afford having serviced for over a year – and start driving. The roads are coated with ice so thick that it feels like your car skates across the surface. The highway's even worse, and you can barely see because the streaks of ice form a white wall in the glare of your headlights. You should drive more slowly, more cautiously, but you don't. You think that it wouldn't be so bad if you lost control of your car, spun out, and crashed. With any luck, you'd die, and your daughters would believe it was an accident, never guessing it was really suicide, or at least a surrender to the darkness inside you.

But you make it home in one piece a couple of hours later, and the disappointment you feel at still being alive is like a ten-ton weight crushing down on you.

There is no point to my continued existence, you think.

Your agoraphobic mother becomes a ghost who not only haunts a house, she *is* the house. The lake you almost drowned in as a child becomes a setting for many of your stories. Your Uncle Red's corpse – or more to the point, the Great Nothing it represents – becomes the dark force of entropy which lies at the center of your fiction. And entropy, of course, is just another name for your old foe, Time. The rest of it – your cancer, the divorce, the guilt over failing your daughters, the women you couldn't connect with – they're all there in your words, sometimes obvious, usually not. Your life is a funhouse mirror, and you look upon the distortions in the glass, and you write.

If you want to be a horror writer, answer questions from people, like *Where do you get your ideas?* and *How can such a pleasant person write stuff so dark?* And the kicker: *When are you going to write something real? You know, something true and meaningful?*

You'll stand there, Black Dog growling at your side, the taste of lake water on your tongue, still and quiet as a corpse inside, and you'll smile.

CONTRIBUTORS

Giuseppe Balestra aka **GB** is a young illustrator based in Italy. He generally works in pen and inks, hatching and stippling, sometime adding digital color. Balestra has provided illustrations for various artistic projects, books, artbooks, comics and posters, both in Europe and in the USA, including *Poster Spy – Alternative Movie Poster Collection* and *Printed in Blood's The Thing: Artbook.*

Justyna Bendyk is studying philosophy. She writes about death, monsters, outcasts, ruins – all of which contain a peculiar, hidden beauty.

Ashley Dioses is a writer of dark poetry and fiction from southern California. Her debut collection of dark traditional poetry, *Diary of a Sorceress*, was released in 2017 from Hippocampus Press. Her poetry has appeared in *Weird Fiction Review, Skelos, Weirdbook, Black Wings VI: New Tales of Lovecraftian Horror*, and others. She is an Active member in the HWA and a member of the SFPA.

Amelia Gorman is a recent transplant to northern California, where she spends a lot of her free time looking for tidepools with her dogs. Her recent poetry appears in *Liminality Magazine* and her fiction is forthcoming in *Sharp & Sugar Tooth* from Upper Rubber Boot Books.

Jill Hand is a member of the Horror Writers Association. Her work has appeared in more than thirty publications and in many anthologies, including *Miskatonic Dreams*, *Test Patterns* and *Beyond the Stars: New Worlds, New Suns*. She is the author of the time travel novels *The Blue Horse* and *Rosina and the Travel Agency*.

Ksenia Korniewska is a reclusive artist, currently residing in Kyiv, Ukraine. She spends most of her waking life exploring her inner blackness, dissecting the abominations she finds within, and transforming their foetid entrails into paintings and drawings. Her work primarily focuses on that delicate state of matter when the form starts to insanely emerge out of the formlessness, commencing the never-ending nightmare of self-recreating corporeality, from which there is no escape.

Øyvind Lauvdahl is a freelance illustrator and sequential artist working and living in Norway. His most current works can be seen at www.instagram.com/lauvdahl.

Carl Lavoie likes Hirschvogel's landscapes, stories by Ron Weighell, and his Polish muse, Zytnia. He lives in Southwestern Ontario.

Rob F. Martin is an ex-evangelical pastor residing in Reading, Pa. His surrealist novella, *The DollKeeper*, was inspired by his autistic daughter, and his short fiction appears in *Test Patterns* and *Ravenwood*. Occasionally, he updates his blog, uncertainvoices.wordpress.com, where he muses on philosophy, religion, and meaning(lessness).

Christopher Mountenay received his PhD in philosophy from

Duquesne University but realized that the life of an academic was too soul-crushing, even for a hardened Schopenhauerian. He has since gone to work directly for the Black Gondolier and voraciously consumes weird fiction. He lives in Pittsburgh with his wife, two cats, and lizard.

Joanna Parypinski is a college English instructor by day and a writer of the dark and strange by night. Her work has appeared in *Nightmare Magazine*, *Haunted Nights* (Penguin Random House), and *The Beauty of Death 2: Death by Water* (Independent Legions), with forthcoming work in *Nightscript Vol. 4* and *Tales from the Lake Vol. 5*. Living in the shadow of an old church that sits atop a hilly cemetery north of Los Angeles, she writes, grades essays, and plays her cello surrounded by the sounds of screaming neighbor children. Visit her website at joannaparypinski.com.

Max D. Stanton is an academic, writer, and morbid oddball who lives in Philadelphia surrounded by animals and books. He increasingly suspects that the animals are plotting against him, and perhaps the books as well. Max has published weird fiction in anthologies including *Corporate Cthulhu*, *Death's Garden*, and *Year's Best Transhuman Sci-Fi 2017*. You can contact him within the Book of Faces and the Great Shrieking of Birds.

Yves Tourigny is a bipedal animal frequently mistaken for a small bear or well-fed raccoon. The product of billions of years of evolutionary pressure and sexual selection, his accomplishments fit comfortably on an index card.

Julie Travis has been a skateboarder, fanzine writer, bassist in various punk bands, psychiatric patient and political activist. A writer of fiction since the early 1990s, her work has been described as "bloodstream" rather than slipstream. Her second short story collection, *We Are All Falling Towards The Centre Of The Earth*, was published by Wapshott Press on this year's Summer Solstice. Find her at www.julietravis.wordpress.com.

Nicole Vasari writes from the US Northeast. She has been published in *The Audient Void*.

Tim Waggoner has published over forty novels and five collections of short stories. He writes original dark fantasy and horror, as well as media tie-ins, and his articles on writing have appeared in numerous publications. He's won the Bram Stoker Award, been a finalist for the Shirley Jackson Award and the Scribe Award, his fiction has received numerous Honorable Mentions in volumes of *Best Horror of the Year*, and he's twice had stories selected for inclusion in volumes of *Year's Best Hardcore Horror*. He's also a full-time tenured professor who teaches creative writing and composition at Sinclair Community College in Dayton, Ohio.

Charles Wilkinson's publications include *The Pain Tree and Other Stories* (London Magazine Editions, 2000). His stories have appeared in *Best Short Stories 1990* (Heinemann), *Best English Short Stories 2* (W.W. Norton, USA), *Best British Short Stories 2015* (Salt) and in genre magazines/anthologies such as *Black Static*, *Supernatural Tales*, *Phantom Drift* (USA), *Bourbon Penn* (USA), *Shadows & Tall Trees* (Canada), *Nightscript* (USA) and *Best Weird*

Fiction 2015 (Undertow Books, Canada). His anthology of strange tales and weird fiction, *A Twist in the Eye*, is now out from Egaeus Press and his second collection from the same publisher is due out this year. He lives in Powys, Wales.

GRIMSCRIBE PRESS